CONTENTS

O9-AIG-920

i

ENGLISH WORKSHOP REVIEW COURSE teaches you important skills involved in writing and speaking standard English. If you are a senior, you will already have studied most of these skills. Nevertheless, you will readily admit that there is still room for improvement in your writing and speech. Even if your writing is grammatically and mechanically correct, you recognize the need for more practice in composition, especially in the construction of sentences which are clear and smooth as well as correct. Of course, you may still be uncertain about mechanics: uses of capital letters and punctuation marks. You may still need drill in grammar and usage.

You should work through Parts One, Two, and Three, studying the lessons in order because they are cumulative. Near the end of each chapter there is a Chapter Review, which is followed by a Cumulative Review. To do well on these review lessons, you should have mastered all the preceding lessons. Some of the Cumulative Reviews (see "Cumulative Review: Standardized Test Form," pp. 104, 124, 145, 190) are written in approximately the form of the most commonly used standardized tests. If you do well on the Reviews, you should do well on the standardized tests your school requires you to take from time to time. At regular intervals you will find lessons on vocabulary and spelling. Each of these is part of a carefully planned, cumulative program which should be studied in the order in which the lessons come.

Part Four is called *Writing Compositions.* There is little value in learning the rules of standard English unless you have opportunities to apply them in writing. Although it is the final section in the book, Part Four should not be left for a few weeks of concentrated composition work at the end of the course but should be used regularly during your study of Parts One, Two, and Three. Your teacher will assign the lessons in Part Four at appropriate times throughout the year.

ENGLISH WORKSHOP REVIEW COURSE will help you to develop your vocabulary, improve your spelling, and use English according to the dictates of modern usage. But the most important thing it will do for you is show you how to improve your writing by careful revision. The book contains a great many exercises on revising passages which are not well written. Through these exercises you will learn what to look for when you are revising your own writing and how to make improvements in it. Your work on the exercises in the book will carry over to the work on your own themes only if you make it do so. If you conscientiously correct and revise your own themes in the same way that you correct and revise the exercises in the book, the quality of your writing will improve.

Part One
A REVIEW OF GRAMMAR TERMS AND MECHANICS

Review of Grammar Terms

This first chapter in Part One begins with a diagnostic test. By taking this test you will reveal to your teacher and to yourself how much of the material in the chapter you remember from your earlier work in English. It is entirely possible, for example, that you already know English grammar terms so well that you will not need to review them in Chapter One. If this should be true, begin your work in the book with Lesson 7, Chapter Review. Perhaps, however, the diagnostic test will reveal competence in some areas of grammar but weaknesses in others. For example, should you demonstrate complete knowledge of the parts of speech and the parts of the sentence base, but not of phrases and clauses, you could easily begin your work with Lesson 4. Use of the diagnostic test will save you from needlessly studying material you already know.

Diagnostic Test

PARTS OF SPEECH In the numbered spaces below each sentence, give the part of speech of the correspondingly numbered underscored words. Use the following abbreviations:

n. = noun	*v.* = verb	*prep.* = preposition	*adj.* = adjective
pron. = pronoun	*adv.* = adverb	*conj.* = conjunction	

(Add 2 points for each correct answer.)

She 1 dreams the 2 dreams of youth.

1 . . . .   2 . . . .

In 3 speech class my 4 speech was praised.

3 . . . .   4 . . . .

1

Do all you can 5 <u>for</u> 6 <u>him</u>, 7 <u>for</u> he needs help.

5 ....   6 ....   7 ....

The test was repeated 8 <u>later</u> 9 <u>because</u> 10 <u>everyone</u> had done 11 <u>badly</u>.

8 ....   9 ....   10 ....   11 ....

She is wearing a 12 <u>dark</u> blue dress.

12 ....

PARTS OF THE SENTENCE BASE

In the numbered spaces below each sentence, write the *subject* (s), *verb* (v), and *complement* (c). Use the following abbreviations to tell the kind (k) of complement: *s.c.* for *subject complement; d.o.* for *direct object;* and *i.o.* for *indirect object.*

Neither of the boys is working.

13 (s)............   14 (v)............

Lydia is always confident.

15 (s)............   16 (v)............   17 (c)............   18 (k)......

Static sometimes spoils radio reception.

19 (s)............   20 (v)............   21 (c)............   22 (k)......

Tomorrow will be a good day.

23 (s)............   24 (v)............   25 (c)............   26 (k)......

My uncle in California gave me a set of golf clubs.

27 (s)............   28 (v)............

29 (c)............   30 (k)............   31 (c)............   32 (k)......

Complete the statements that follow each sentence by writing the appropriate word or words in each numbered blank.

A visitor from the nineteenth century would be amazed at our scientific knowledge.

The two prepositional phrases in this sentence are 33 ....

.... and 34 ....

The first phrase modifies the word 35................ and is therefore a(n) 36................ phrase.

The number of women who join the police force is increasing.

The subordinate clause in this sentence is 37 ....

.... The subject of this clause is 38 ....

The verb is 39 ...., and the complement is 40 ....

2

This kind of complement is called a(n) 41 ....

You are what you eat.

The subordinate clause in this sentence is 42 ....

The subject of the clause is 43 ....; the verb in the clause is

44 ....; the complement in the clause is 45 ....

The complement in the clause is the kind called a(n) 46 ....

.... This clause is used as the part of speech called a(n)

47.................... The whole clause is the kind of complement called

a(n) 48..

When you are ready, give the signal.

The subordinate clause in this sentence is 49 ....

.... The whole clause is used as the part of speech called

a(n) 50 ....

LESSON 1

Nouns, Pronouns, Adjectives

A <u>noun</u> is a word used to name a person, place, thing, or idea.

A <u>proper noun</u> names a particular person, place, thing, or idea. A <u>common noun</u> does not name a particular person, place, thing, or idea. A proper noun begins with a capital letter.

PROPER NOUN	COMMON NOUN
St. Louis	city
Margaret Mead	woman
Chevrolet	automobile
Republican	political party

A <u>pronoun</u> is a word used in place of a noun. It may stand for a person, place, thing, or idea.

Bernice Brown was elected president. She had been treasurer. (In the second sentence the pronoun *she* is used in place of the noun *Bernice Brown.*)

The boys spent all their money on an old car. Later they were sorry they had bought it. (The pronouns *their* and *they* are used in place of the noun *boys;* the pronoun *it* is used in place of the noun *car.*)

Review the following classification of pronouns, and familiarize yourself with the words in each list. The starred words on the lists are also used as adjectives.

3

I, me	he, him	it	they, them
you	she, her	we, us	

POSSESSIVE FORMS OF THE PERSONAL PRONOUNS

my, mine	his	its	their, theirs
your, yours	her, hers	our, ours	

Relative pronouns are used to introduce subordinate clauses.
Interrogative pronouns are used in questions.

RELATIVE AND INTERROGATIVE PRONOUNS

who	*which	*what
whom	*that	whose

DEMONSTRATIVE PRONOUNS (point out *which one*)

*this	*these	*that	*those

INDEFINITE PRONOUNS

*all	*each	*many	*one
*any	*either	*neither	*several
anybody	everybody	nobody	*some
anyone	everyone	none	somebody
*both	*few	no one	someone

An adjective is a word used to modify a noun or a pronoun.

Modify means to describe, to make the meaning of a word more definite. An adjective may modify a noun or a pronoun in one of three ways:

1. by telling *what kind: green* hat, *small* car, *French* people
2. by pointing out *which one: this* argument, *that* picture
3. by telling *how many: three* months, *many* letters

Adjectives, which usually precede the words they modify, may also come after.

EXAMPLE   A yacht, sleek and white, was leaving the harbor.

An adjective may be separated by a verb from the word it modifies.

The day seemed endless.   (*endless* day)

You are wrong.   (*wrong* you)

EXERCISE   In this exercise some of the nouns, pronouns, and adjectives are italicized and numbered. Write in the numbered space what part of speech (*noun,*

4

pron., or *adj.*) each word is. If the word is a pronoun, write in the second space the noun it stands for. If the word is an adjective, write the word it modifies. (Add 4 points for each correct item.)

a. (1) *Guidance* counselors are advising (2) *senior* students to hesitate before (3) *they* enroll in education (4) *courses.*

(1) . . . .
(2) . . . .
(3) . . . .
(4) . . . .

b. The (5) *steady* drop in the (6) *rate* of births in the (7) *late* sixties and early seventies has reduced the number of children (8) *who* are entering school.

(5) . . . .
(6) . . . .
(7) . . . .

(8) . . . .

c. Because experts expect the (9) *downward* trend to continue, (10) *they* predict (11) *smaller* enrollments throughout the seventies.

(9) . . . .
(10) . . . .
(11) . . . .

d. Superintendent Gold says that (12) *she* recognizes (13) *this* decline in students, and (14) *it* must result in a need for fewer teachers.

(12) . . . .
(13) . . . .
(14) . . . .

e. (15) *We* Americans have been unable to increase (16) *our* school budgets (17) *which* pay teachers' salaries.

(15) . . . .

(16) . . . .
(17) . . . .

f. (18) *Less* money for salaries means a (19) *decline* in

(18) . . . .
(19) . . . .

new jobs and an (20) *older*   (20) ....

population of teachers.

g. At the same time that our colleges have been training more (21) *good* teachers,   (21) ....

the number of jobs for (22)   (22) ....

them has been declining.

h. These (23) *adverse* condi-   (23) ....

tions will discourage stu-

dents (24) *who* would like   (24) ....

to be teachers, and (25)   (25) ....

many may choose another

profession.

Verbs, Adverbs, Conjunctions

A verb is a word that expresses action or helps to make a statement.

The action expressed by a verb may be action involving actual physical motion, or it may be action performed by the mind; that is, action may be either physical or mental. The verb *believe* expresses mental action.

Verbs which do not express action are called *linking verbs* when they act as a link between the subject and a noun, pronoun, or adjective that describes or identifies the subject. In acting as a link, they help to make a statement.[1]

Bertha **was** successful. (*Was* helps to make a statement about Bertha; it links *Bertha* and *successful*; it does not express action.)

EXAMPLES   The room **seems** warm.   Miles **will be** the teacher.
              She **is** the winner.   That soup **tastes** salty.

The commonly used linking verbs are the forms of the verb *be* (*am, is, are, was, were,* and verbs of more than one word ending in *be* or *been*). Often the following words are used as linking verbs: *appear, become, feel, grow, look, remain, seem, smell, sound, stay, taste.*[2]

---

[1] Linking verbs are sometimes called "state-of-being" verbs.
[2] Some of these linking verbs may also be action words: I *smell* the dinner. (action) The dinner *smells* good. (linking)

         © 1977 HBJ

A verb may be made up of more than one word. The parts of such a verb may be separated by other words.

EXAMPLES **Have** you **done** your homework?   You **could** at least **try**.
We **did** not **read** the assignment.   Anna **was** recently **promoted**.

EXERCISE A Underline the twenty verbs in the following sentences. Above each action verb, write *A;* above each linking verb, write *L*. Many of the verbs consist of more than one word. The word *not* is not a verb. (Add 5 points for each correctly marked verb.)

1. Look at the map, and tell me what town we are approaching.

2. This map could be clearer; it does not show the new expressway.

3. Find a newer map among the ones that are available.

4. You can ask directions when we come to a gas station.

5. I enjoy good maps because they satisfy my curiosity.

6. Could you draw a map of your home town?

7. A climate map looks different from a political map, but it is not as interesting to me.

8. Accurate maps and charts are important to sailors and aviators, who must be expert map readers.

9. On the map the border country seems hilly, and the coastal area appears flat.

10. The deposits of a river may build a delta, which forms at the mouth of the river.

An adverb is a word used to modify a verb, an adjective, or another adverb.

As the modifier of a verb, an adverb may tell *how, when, where,* or *to what extent* the action of the verb is done.

EXAMPLES Billie Jean King played well. (played *how*)

We will leave early. (will leave *when*)

I have been there. (have been *where*)

We went far. (went *to what extent*)

An adverb may modify an adjective.

EXAMPLE The speech was unexpectedly brief.

An adverb may modify another adverb.

EXAMPLE The orchestra played unusually well.

7

EXERCISE B Circle each of the ten adverbs in the following sentences and draw an arrow to the word the adverb modifies. (Add 5 points for each correct answer.)

1. Al Young generously offered to take us in his boat to try our new water skis.

2. Although inexperienced, we really believed we could skim gracefully over the water.

3. Soon we were roaring toward the ski area; there we dropped Cheryl overboard with the skis and tow rope.

4. When Cheryl was ready, Al gunned the motor hard, and Cheryl rose suddenly above the surface.

5. She reeled wildly to the right and then careened to the left before plunging into the boat's wake.

A **conjunction** is a word that joins words and groups of words.

The three kinds of conjunctions are (1) coordinating conjunctions, (2) subordinating conjunctions, and (3) correlative conjunctions. When the words in the following lists join words or groups of words, they are conjunctions.

1. Coordinating conjunctions: *and, but, or, nor.*
2. Subordinating conjunctions:

after	because	so that	when
although	before	than	whenever
as	if	though	where
as if	in order that	unless	wherever
as long as	since	until	while
as though			

3. Correlative conjunctions: *either . . . or; neither . . . nor; both . . . and; not only . . . but (also); whether . . . or.* Correlative conjunctions are always used in pairs.

EXERCISE C The italicized verbs, adverbs, and conjunctions in the following sentences are numbered and also listed below each sentence. In the first space after each word in the list, tell what part of speech it is. In the second space, give information as follows: if the word is a verb, tell whether it is an action verb or a linking verb (*A* or *L*); if the word is an adverb, tell what word it modifies; if the word is a conjunction, tell what kind of conjunction it is. (Add 5 points for each correct item.)

A. (1) *Later* I (2) *saw* the principal (3) *and* explained our problem.

	Part of Speech	Information
(1) Later	*adv.*	*saw*
(2) saw	*verb*	*a*
(3) and	*conj.*	*coordinating*

a. "(1) *Make* haste (2) *slowly*" (3) *is* good advice, (4) *but* young people (5) *seldom* (6) *follow* it.

(1) Make . . . .

(2) slowly . . . .

(3) is . . . .

(4) but . . . .

(5) seldom . . . .

(6) follow . . . .

b. Hurry (7) *not only* (8) *produces* imperfect results, *but also* (9) *may be* (10) *extremely* dangerous.

(7) not only . . . but also . . . .

(8) produces . . . .

(9) may be . . . .

(10) extremely . . . .

c. (11) *As* highway signs (12) *frequently* (13) *remind* us, speed (14) *kills.*

(11) As . . . .

(12) frequently . . . .

(13) remind . . . .

(14) kills . . . .

d. Industrial experts (15) *know* (16) *well* that accidents (17) *are caused* by carelessness, (18) *and* carelessness (19) *is* (20) *often* due to haste.

(15) know . . . .

(16) well . . . .

(17) are caused . . . .

(18) and . . . .

(19) is . . . .

(20) often . . . .

LESSON 3

Subject, Verb, Complements

Every sentence consists of two parts: the <u>subject</u> and the <u>predicate</u>. The subject of a sentence is that part about which something is being said. The <u>predicate</u> is that part which says something about the subject.

SUBJECT	PREDICATE
The old mansion	was built in 1893.

Although the subject normally precedes the predicate (verb), it may follow the predicate.

PREDICATE   SUBJECT

At the head of the stairs stood   my father.

The whole subject is called the *complete subject;* the whole predicate is called the *complete predicate*.

Simple Subject and Simple Predicate The *simple subject* is the main word or group of words in the complete subject. The simple subjects in the sentences above are *mansion* and *father*.

The *simple predicate* is the main word or group of words in the complete predicate. It is usually referred to simply as the *verb*. The simple predicates in the sentences above are *was built* and *stood*.

Note 1: When the simple predicate consists of more than one word, these words may be separated by other words.

EXAMPLE **Have** you **been** away? (Simple predicate: *have been*)

Note 2: In a sentence expressing a command or a request, the simple subject is understood to be the word *you,* although *you* does not appear in the sentence.

EXAMPLE Write your homework in ink. (Simple subject: *you* [Write])

Note 3: A simple subject and a simple predicate may be compound; that is, they may consist of two or more words connected by *and* or *or*.

EXAMPLE Fred and I came early and prepared the field. (Compound subject: *Fred, I;* compound verb: *came, prepared*)

Note 4: The simple subject is never in a prepositional phrase.

EXAMPLE **Neither** of the candidates **impresses** me. (The sentence does not say *candidates impress;* it says *neither impresses. Candidates* is in a prepositional phrase.)

EXERCISE A Draw one line under the simple subject and two lines under the simple predicate (verb) in each of the following sentences. In a command or request, add the simple subject *you.* You will be able to identify the subject more easily if you cross out the prepositional phrases. (Add 10 points for each correctly marked sentence.)

A. In a plane, always fasten your seat belt before take off. *(you)*

1. Most drivers regularly obey traffic laws.

2. Obedience to the law assures your own safety.

3. Stop at every stop sign and look in both directions.

4. Above the roar of traffic shrilled a traffic controller's whistle.

5. Her direction helps to keep traffic moving.

6. One of the results of accidents is a heavy repair bill.

7. Never drive faster than the speed limit.

8. Did you and Frank take your driving test on Saturday?

9. Father and Mother have always been expert drivers.

10. Joe took the car without permission and ran into a tree.

COMPLEMENTS

The simple subject and simple predicate, or verb, are essential parts of all sentences. Many sentences, however, have a third basic part, a *complement,* or completer, which completes the meaning begun by the subject and verb. There are four kinds of complements: the *direct object,* the *indirect object,* the *predicate nominative,* and the *predicate adjective.* The predicate nominative and predicate adjective are also called *subject complements* because they refer to the subject.

SIMPLE SUBJECT	VERB	COMPLEMENT
The *teacher*	*gave*	the **answers**. (direct object)
The *teacher*	*gave*	**him** the answers. (indirect object)
My *brother*	*is*	a **pianist**. (predicate nominative)
Her *grades*	*have been*	**satisfactory**. (predicate adjective)

Direct Object   The direct object is a word or group of words that receives the action of the verb or shows the result of the action. It answers the question *whom* or *what* after an action verb.

EXAMPLES   Unfortunately I broke the window.

Together we lifted the box.

Who made this table?

Indirect Object   The indirect object precedes the direct object and usually tells to whom or for whom the action of the verb is done.

EXAMPLES   I gave **her** your message.   (*to* her: *her* is the indirect object; *message* is the direct object)
The machine saved **us** hours of work.   (*for* us: *us* is the indirect object; *hours* is the direct object)

Direct and indirect objects follow action verbs only. Since, like subjects, they are never found in a prepositional phrase, they are never preceded by a preposition.

Predicate Nominative   A predicate nominative is a noun or pronoun in the predicate which refers to the same thing as the subject of the verb. It follows a linking verb.

11

EXAMPLES She is an extremely efficient **accountant**. (accountant = she)

Arnold seemed to be a good **boy**. (boy = Arnold)

Predicate Adjective A predicate adjective is an adjective in the predicate which *modifies* the subject of the verb. It follows a linking verb.

EXAMPLES The game was unusually **fast**. (*fast* game)

You look **tired**. (*tired* you)

Predicate nominatives usually follow only the verb *be: am, is, are, was, were,* and all verbs ending in *be* or *been* (*may be, have been,* etc.).

Predicate adjectives follow the verb *be* or one of the other linking verbs: *appear, become, feel, grow, look, remain, seem, smell, sound, stay, taste.*

EXERCISE B In the following sentences, the complements are listed at the right. After each, tell what kind of complement it is: direct object (*d.o.*), indirect object (*i.o.*), predicate nominative (*p.n.*), or predicate adjective (*p.a.*). (Add 10 points for each correct answer.)

a. Anaïs Nin was a dancer for a while.   (1) dancer   . . . . .

b. Later she abandoned that career.   (2) career   . . . . .

c. Her father did not give Anaïs   (3) Anaïs   . . . . .

encouragement.   (4) encouragement   . . . . .

d. She became a writer instead.   (5) writer   . . . . .

e. She seemed happier when writing.   (6) happier   . . . . .

f. She had always kept a diary.   (7) diary   . . . . .

g. The diary remained important to her.   (8) important   . . . . .

h. Eventually she offered her publishers   (9) publishers   . . . . .

the diary.   (10) diary   . . . . .

REVIEW EXERCISE Label the verbs, subjects, and complements in the following sentences. Use *s.* (subject); *v.* (verb); *d.o.* (direct object); *i.o.* (indirect object); *p.a.* (predicate adjective); *p.n.* (predicate nominative). (Add 10 points for each correct sentence.)

s. v. v. i.o. d.o.

A. I have taken her a box of candy.

1. Mrs. Bell did not give us a homework assignment.

2. Now you can do some of those new assignments.

3. Neither of those lessons is difficult.

4. Has anyone done the fifth problem in today's lesson?

12

5. Buffy Sainte-Marie certainly is one of my favorite folk singers.

6. Because of her height she seems very slender.

7. Studying at home has always been an irksome task.

8. My aunt in Seattle sent me a dictionary.

9. Give José your class notes.

10. Strange and bewildering are the ways of adolescents.

Prepositions and Phrases

A preposition is a word used to show the relation of a noun or pronoun that follows it to some other word in the sentence.

In the sentence *The book is on the table,* the word *on* shows the relationship of the book to the table. Similarly, the prepositions *under, behind, beside, in, near,* etc., would indicate other relationships between book and table.

The following words are commonly used as prepositions:

about	behind	concerning	of	toward
above	below	down	off	under
across	beneath	during	on	underneath
after	beside	except	over	until
against	besides	for	past	up
along	between	from	since	upon
among	beyond	in	through	with
around	but (meaning	into	throughout	within
at	*except*)	like	to	without
before	by			

A preposition always appears in a phrase, usually at the beginning. The noun or pronoun at the end of the *prepositional phrase* is the *object* of the preposition.

A phrase is a group of words used as a single part of speech and not containing a subject and its verb.

PREPOSITIONAL PHRASES

in the closet	*by* the window	*after* the election
for the present	*of* the students	*with* a friend
from Chicago	*behind* him	*beneath* the bridge

A prepositional phrase used as an adjective is an adjective phrase.

13

In the following sentences the phrases printed in red modify nouns. They are therefore adjective phrases.

EXAMPLES   Our struggle **against nature** is unending.

·   The guard **at the entrance** let us in.

A phrase may modify a word in another phrase.

EXAMPLE   At the end **of the day** everyone was tired. (The adjective phrase *of the day* modifies the noun *end*, which is in the preceding phrase *at the end*.)

A prepositional phrase used as an adverb is an <u>adverb phrase</u>.

EXAMPLES   Please call **in the morning**   (*in the morning* tells *when*)

We spent the afternoon **at the museum**.   (*at the museum* tells *where*)

Broken china can be mended **with glue**.   (*with glue* tells *how*)

EXERCISE A   Place parentheses around the adjective and adverb phrases in each of the following sentences. Draw an arrow to the word the phrase modifies. Over the phrase, name the kind of phrase by writing *adj.* or *adv.* (Add 10 points for each correctly marked phrase.)

A. The game begins *(at two o'clock).* *adv.*

1. The game on Saturday drew the largest crowd of the season.

2. At noon we got in the line at the box office.

3. In the fourth inning Alex reached for a home-run ball.

4. The ball bounced from his hand into the lap of another spectator.

VERBALS AND VERBAL PHRASES

Verbals are of three kinds: the *participle*, the *gerund*, and the *infinitive*. These constructions are called verbals because they are formed from verbs and, to some extent, act as verbs. They are not verbs, however, but words which combine the functions of two parts of speech.

A <u>participle</u> is a word which is formed from a verb and used as an adjective.

EXAMPLES   The **marching** band rehearses daily.

Marching, the band thrilled the crowd.

The participle *marching* is formed from the verb *march;* like an adjective, it modifies the noun *band.*

14

RELATIVE PRONOUNS

who   whom   whose   which   what   that

SUBORDINATING CONJUNCTIONS[1]

after	as long as	if	than	whenever
although	as though	in order that	unless	where
as	because	since	until	wherever
as if	before	so that	when	while

EXAMPLES OF SUBORDINATE CLAUSES

I spoke to a woman who was standing near me.

Did you believe what Sean told you?

The book that you asked for has been lost.

Although we often quarrel, we are very good friends.

If I help you, will you help me?

I'll give Jim your message when I see him.

Yvonne was chosen because she is the most capable.

EXERCISE A   Underline the subordinate clause in each sentence. Write *v* above the verb and *s* above the subject in each underlined clause. If the verb consists of more than one word, write *v* above every word of the verb. (Add 10 points for each correctly marked sentence.)

A. As the President had predicted, the program was approved by Congress.

 1. I experienced every minor accident that can happen to a child.

 2. The person whose car blocked the driveway could not be found.

 3. The direction of the wind is the direction from which it blows.

 4. Fran has a happy disposition that puts everyone at ease.

 5. Luckily, we found a gas station which was still open.

 6. I had no interest in classical music until I joined the orchestra.

 7. Whenever the motor is running, the garage doors should be open.

 8. Only a diamond can cut a diamond because nothing else is so hard.

 9. Helen plays the piano well although she has never taken lessons.

10. Although we usually bake our own cakes, this is a store cake.

REVIEW EXERCISE   Underline the subordinate clauses in the following sentences. Write *s* above the subject and *v* above the verb in each subordinate clause. Put

[1] Many of these words may also be used as prepositions. The function of a word always determines its part of speech.

parentheses around the adjective and adverb phrases in each sentence. Draw an arrow to the word each phrase modifies. Phrases, of course, frequently appear within clauses. (Add 4 points for each correctly marked clause and phrase.)

A. If you do not have a copy (of the book), notify me (at once).

1. The plane that we took to Italy was enormous.

2. Although we flew at night, we had only twenty minutes of real darkness.

3. Because we were going east, sunrise came before midnight.

4. Beneath us the clouds, which reflected the rapidly rising sun, were beautiful.

5. While most of the passengers tried to sleep, I was fascinated by the clouds and sky.

6. Before breakfast, which was served at two o'clock, we caught our first sight of land.

7. The Rome airport is named for Leonardo da Vinci, who designed a flying machine in the year 1500.

8. When we landed, the time in Rome was 9:00 A.M., which was 3:00 A.M. in New York.

9. Our return flight, which we made in the daytime, took a little longer.

THE KINDS OF SENTENCES ACCORDING TO THEIR STRUCTURE

A simple sentence is a sentence with one independent clause and no subordinate clauses.

EXAMPLE   In the fourth quarter the excitement of the crowd rose to fever pitch.

Note: A simple sentence may have two subjects and two verbs, provided it does not consist of more than one independent clause.

EXAMPLE   Frank and Marian took care of the children and did the cooking.
(Here are a compound subject—two subjects joined by *and*—and a compound verb. Together they make up one independent clause.)

A compound sentence is a sentence with two or more independent clauses but no subordinate clauses.

EXAMPLE   In the fourth quarter the excitement of the crowd rose to fever pitch, and everybody stood up.

A complex sentence is a sentence with one independent clause and one or more subordinate clauses.

EXAMPLE   In the fourth quarter the <u>excitement</u> of the crowd <u>rose</u> to fever pitch when our <u>team</u> <u>recovered</u> a fumble

A compound-complex sentence is a sentence with two or more independent clauses and one or more subordinate clauses.

EXAMPLE   In the fourth quarter the <u>excitement</u> of the crowd <u>rose</u> to fever pitch, and <u>everyone</u> <u>stood</u> up when our <u>team</u> <u>recovered</u> a fumble

EXERCISE B   Draw one line under each independent clause and two lines under each subordinate clause in the following sentences. Referring to the preceding definitions, tell in the space at the right what kind each sentence is: *Simple—S; Compound —Cd; Complex—Cx; Compound-Complex—Cd-Cx.* (Add 10 points for each correctly marked sentence.)

1. Shirley Chisholm grew up in Brooklyn, where she graduated from Brooklyn College. . . . .

2. She went to graduate school and became a teacher. . . . .

3. After graduation Mrs. Chisholm taught children and joined voluntary organizations and local political clubs. . . . .

4. She worked for the reform of the political parties, and she was concerned about serving the needs of more citizens. . . . .

5. Political action was needed, and Mrs. Chisholm decided to run for office, although many said she would lose. . . . .

6. In 1964 she ran for the New York State Assembly and won. . . . .

7. She was not afraid to try, and her victory showed others that hard work and dedication can lead to success. . . . .

8. Since she was elected to Congress in 1968, she has fought for the needs of the poor and the cities. . . . .

9. In 1972 she announced her candidacy for the Presidency, but her party did not give her the nomination. . . . .

10. Mrs. Chisholm wrote an autobiography called *Unbought and Unbossed,* which was published in 1970. . . . .

Adjective, Adverb, and Noun Clauses

Like phrases, subordinate clauses are used as a single part of speech.

An <u>adjective clause</u> is a subordinate clause which—like an adjective—modifies a noun or a pronoun. Usually it identifies or points out *which one*.

EXAMPLES   Students who are gifted receive advanced instruction.   (tells *which students*)

I read the book that you recommended.   (tells *which book*)

We knew everyone who was present.   (identifies *everyone*)

Adjective clauses are usually (not always) introduced by the words *who, whom, whose, which, that.*

An <u>adverb clause</u> is a subordinate clause which is used as an adverb.

EXAMPLES   Elena acted as though she were angry.   (tells *how*)

When the mail arrived, we distributed it.   (tells *when*)

The doctor goes wherever she is needed.   (tells *where*)

I came because you sent for me.   (tells *why*)

If you see Dick, let me know.   (tells *under what conditions*)

You are not so tall as I am.   (clause modifying an adjective)

She played better than I did.   (clause modifying an adverb)

Most adverb clauses are introduced by subordinating conjunctions (see p. 17).

A <u>noun clause</u> is a subordinate clause used as a noun.

EXAMPLES   Whoever is just will be respected.   (The noun clause is the subject of the verb *will be respected*. It tells *who* will be respected.)

I understand what he is doing.   (The noun clause is the object of the verb *understand*. It tells *what* I understand.)

EXERCISE A   Each sentence in this exercise contains a subordinate clause. Draw a line under the subordinate clause. Write *v* over the verb and *s* over its subject. In the first column, state what the clause tells—*which one* or *what kind; how, when, where, why, under what conditions; who* or *what*. In the second column, state what kind of clause it is—*adj., adv.,* or *noun.* You will need to remember these facts:

1. Adjective clauses usually identify someone or something. They tell *which one* or *what kind.*

20

2. Adverb clauses usually tell *how, where, when, why,* or *under what conditions.*

3. Noun clauses are used as subjects, objects, or predicate nominatives. They tell *who* or *what.*

(Add 2 points for each correct answer.)

	Tells	Kind
A. He had a plan <u>which was excellent</u>.	*what kind*	*adj.*
B. <u>After they had heard the plan</u>, they approved it.	*when*	*adv.*
C. I know <u>who called you</u>.	*what*	*noun*
1. While our parents played cards, we watched television.	. . . .	. . . .
2. I will pay whatever you ask.	. . . .	. . . .
3. Ask for the book that I reserved.	. . . .	. . . .
4. A letter which is mailed today will be delivered in the city tomorrow.	. . . .	. . . .
5. If there is any delay, we will notify you.	. . . .	. . . .
6. Their taxi driver, who did not understand English, took them to the wrong airport.	. . . .	. . . .
7. Why the planes crashed remains a mystery.	. . . .	. . . .
8. Ann was calm because she had practiced.	. . . .	. . . .
9. He looked as though he were tired.	. . . .	. . . .
10. The President is carefully guarded wherever he goes.	. . . .	. . . .

EXERCISE B Underline the subordinate clause in each sentence. Determine how it is used. In the space at the right, tell whether it is an adjective, adverb, or noun clause. Remember that a clause contains a verb and its subject. (Add 10 points for each correctly marked sentence.)

1. The yoga postures that you are doing are simple. . . . .

2. They are part of an ancient discipline that still works. . . . .

3. You should learn what each posture does for you. . . . .

4. As you do the movements, you control your breathing. . . . .

21

5. That you relax between postures is important. . . . .

6. If you do the postures daily, you will improve rapidly. . . . .

7. You will feel relaxed after you exercise. . . . .

8. Yogis are teachers who have achieved great mastery. . . . .

9. Their accomplishments are what inspire their students. . . . .

10. Yogis eat carefully because diet affects health. . . . .

Chapter Review

SUMMARY TEST ON GRAMMAR TERMS The following test covers most of the grammar terms reviewed in this chapter. The questions below each sentence are based on the words and word groups in the sentence. In each question, select the correct answer and write its letter in the space at the right. (Add 4 points for each correct answer.)

a. The Geneva Convention, which governs the treatment of prisoners of war, was adopted at a conference of thirty-five nations in Geneva in 1906.

1. The simple subject is (a) treatment, (b) which, (c) governs, (d) Geneva Convention. . . . .

2. The verb, or simple predicate, is (a) governs, (b) was adopted, (c) conference, (d) treatment. . . . .

3. *which* is (a) preposition, (b) adjective, (c) relative pronoun, (d) subordinating conjunction. . . . .

4. *at a conference* is (a) adverb clause, (b) adverb phrase, (c) adjective phrase, (d) adjective clause. . . . .

b. This new international agreement supplemented an earlier convention dealing with the humane treatment of the wounded on the battlefield.

5. *convention* is (a) direct object, (b) indirect object, (c) predicate nominative, (d) predicate adjective. . . . .

6. *dealing* is (a) verb, (b) participle, (c) gerund, (d) preposition. . . . .

7. *of the wounded* is (a) adjective phrase, (b) adverb phrase, (c) adverb clause, (d) adjective clause. . . . .

8. *earlier* is (a) verb, (b) adverb, (c) adjective, (d) noun. . . . .

c. Nations sometimes agree on the rules of war, but they seem unable to agree on the outlawing of war.

9. The sentence is (a) complex, (b) simple, (c) compound, (d) compound-complex. . . . .

10. *to agree* is (a) participle, (b) infinitive, (c) verb, (d) gerund. . . . .
11. *Nations sometimes agree on the rules of war* is (a) phrase, (b) subordinate clause, (c) independent clause, (d) infinitive. . . . .
12. *sometimes* is (a) noun, (b) adjective, (c) adverb, (d) preposition. . . . .
13. *but* is (a) preposition, (b) adverb, (c) adjective, (d) coordinating conjunction. . . . .
14. *outlawing of war* is (a) adjective phrase, (b) adverb phrase, (c) participial phrase, (d) gerund phrase. . . . .
15. *on the rules* is (a) clause, (b) adverb phrase, (c) adjective phrase, (d) complement. . . . .
16. *seem* is (a) noun, (b) action verb, (c) linking verb, (d) adjective. . . . .

d. A pact which did renounce war was the Kellogg-Briand Treaty, which was signed in 1929 by sixty-two powers.

17. The simple predicate is (a) did, (b) was, (c) powers, (d) signed. . . . .
18. *Kellogg-Briand Treaty* is (a) direct object, (b) predicate adjective, (c) predicate nominative, (d) pronoun. . . . .
19. This sentence is (a) simple, (b) compound, (c) complex, (d) compound-complex. . . . .
20. *which did renounce war* is (a) independent clause, (b) adverb clause, (c) adjective clause, (d) adjective phrase. . . . .

e. Although the League of Nations failed to prevent war, most nations still believed that an international organization was necessary.

21. The simple subject is (a) that, (b) most, (c) League of Nations, (d) nations. . . . .
22. *Although the League of Nations failed to prevent war* is (a) adverb clause, (b) adverb phrase, (c) independent clause, (d) adjective phrase. . . . .
23. *that an international organization was necessary* is (a) adjective clause, (b) adverb clause, (c) independent clause, (d) noun clause. . . . .
24. *Although* is (a) preposition, (b) subordinating conjunction, (c) adverb, (d) correlative conjunction. . . . .
25. *necessary* is (a) direct object, (b) predicate adjective, (c) predicate nominative, (d) adverb. . . . .

Building Vocabulary

Research has shown conclusively that people can enlarge their vocabularies by following a systematic program of word study. College entrance tests, army tests, achievement and intelligence tests, in general, stress vocabulary. More important, pleasure in reading and in conversing with others, even how well one succeeds in a business or profession, may be in direct proportion to one's vocabulary.

The words in the fourteen vocabulary lessons in this book have been chosen because, although in common use, they are not necessarily words that you will just naturally "pick up." They are not easy words, but neither are they technical words related to special subjects.

Only the most common meanings of the words are given in these vocabulary lessons. The exercises will help you to fix the words in your mind. Since some of the exercises are reviews, you will be expected to remember, as you proceed, the words learned in preceding vocabulary lessons.

Procedure

1. Learn to pronounce the word, using, if necessary, the charts on pages 248 and 249.

2. Note the part of speech.

3. Study and memorize the definition and synonyms.

4. Learn other forms of the word if any are given.

5. Cover the definitions with a sheet of paper and try to say over to yourself the meaning of each word. Try to use the word in a sentence of your own.

6. Do the exercises thoughtfully.

abstain /ab stăn/, *v.* To refrain from something voluntarily, especially from satisfying one's appetites. Used with *from: Advised by her doctor to abstain from smoking, she broke herself of the habit.* The derivation of this word will help you to remember its meaning. The Latin prefix *ab–* means *from* or *off.* The Latin word *tenere* means *hold;* hence the meaning of *abtenere,* which gives us our word *abstain,* is *to hold off.* —**abstinent** or **abstemious,** *adj.* **abstinence,** *n. If abstinence didn't require will power, I would be a more abstinent (abstemious) person.*

beneficent /bə néf ə sənt/, *adj.* Doing good. Closely related to *beneficial, beneficent* is used to describe a good deed: *His beneficent acts are typical of his thoughtful and generous nature.* A related noun is **benefactor,** which means the person who does a beneficent act for someone: *The name of Pip's benefactor, the man who provided for Pip's education, was kept a secret.*

candid /kán did/, *adj.* Frank; straightforward; sincere. Candid people say what they think. They do not avoid issues but express their beliefs openly and in a straightforward way: *You always know where you stand with Pearl because she is so candid.*

coerce /kō úrs/, *v.* To compel, to force: *Not*

unless she is coerced will Andrea do her homework.—**coercion,** *n. Coercion by the military is only a temporary hindrance to rebellion.*

dubious /dū́ bē əs/, *adj.* Doubtful, uncertain: If you are not sure of a man's sincerity, you may say that *he is a man of dubious sincerity.* When you use *dubious,* you are suggesting that someone is not sincere. Hence *dubious* suggests that something is probably bad: *a person of dubious character,* etc.

fallacy /fál ə sē/, *n.* A false idea; mistaken belief; error—particularly an error in thinking: *The belief that the world is flat was a fallacy corrected by daring voyages.* When a person reasons illogically, the error in thinking is a *fallacy.* Point out the *fallacy* in the following statement: *The sea is blue and salty; salt makes the sea blue.*—**fallacious,** *adj. Fallacious reasoning leads to an incorrect conclusion.*

indolence /ín də ləns/, *n.* Love of ease and inactivity; laziness: *Indolence is a frequent cause of failure.*—**indolent,** *adj. In the hot weather, people become indolent.*

lucid /lū sid/, *adj.* Clear; easily understood: *The essay was written in such a lucid style that we had no trouble understanding it.* —**lucidity,** *n.*

nostalgia /nos tál jə/, *n.* A longing for experiences, things, or people from the past: *Separated from her native surroundings for many years, she found that her nostalgia grew until it became unbearable.*—**nostalgic**, *adj.*

precarious /pri kár ē əs/, *adj.* Insecure; unsafe; dangerous: *Caught on a ledge between the cliff and the rising tide, we were in a precarious position.*

EXERCISE A Write before each word the letter of its synonym from the list at the right. (Add 10 points for each correct answer.)

.... 1. candid
.... 2. dubious
.... 3. indolence
.... 4. coerce
.... 5. beneficent
.... 6. lucid
.... 7. nostalgia
.... 8. abstain
.... 9. precarious
.... 10. fallacy

a. to refrain from
b. doing good
c. frank, straightforward
d. clear
e. doubtful
f. to compel, force
g. a false idea, error
h. laziness
i. longing for the past
j. unsafe

EXERCISE B Each numbered blank in the sentences below can be filled by one of the ten words in this lesson or by a variant form of one of the words. Write in each blank the proper word. Some words are used more than once. (Add 5 points for each correct answer.)

a. Sensing a (1)............................. in Mr. Sim's reasoning, the committee considered his suggestions to be of (2).................... value.

b. Because of her (3)......................... nature, Mary had to be (4)......................... into working steadily.

c. My (5)....................... opinion is that for the sake of your figure you should (6)....................... from eating sweets and starches.

d. By their many (7)........................... acts, my new friends helped me to forget the past, but still when I thought of the joys of former days and places I was filled with (8)...........................

e. Mr. Stout is a superior teacher; his explanations are always (9)........ ...., and he never has to resort to (10) .... of even his most (11)....................... students.

f. Mrs. Sears's (12)......................... from rich foods during her illness has been most remarkable.

g. Although your telegram was far from (13).........................,
   I gathered that you were worried about the (14).....................
   position in which you found yourself.

h. Marian's (15).......................... criticism of our work may have
   been sincere, but it proved of (16)........................... worth
   because it annoyed so many people.

i. Penniless in a strange country, I was in (17).........................
   circumstances; and, as I recalled my misfortunes since leaving home, I
   was filled with self-pity and (18)...........................

j. The (19)......................... in Boyd's reputation as a (20)....
   .... is that his generosity usually has a selfish motive.

A Note on Spelling

Writing may be thought of as a way of recording the sounds of speech by the use of symbols that represent those sounds. The letters in our alphabet are the symbols we use to represent our speech sounds. If we had a different letter for each sound, spelling would be easy; just a matter of knowing which letter to use for each speech sound. Unfortunately, English spelling is not that simple. There are more sounds than there are letters in the alphabet to represent them, and so the task of learning to spell in our language is somewhat complicated.

The complications, however, may be partially overcome by becoming aware of, and learning, the many *spelling patterns* that do exist. These patterns involve the use of various combinations of letters of the alphabet to spell certain sounds.

To show the *sounds* of a word, rather than the letters, a special phonetic alphabet has been developed. Using this phonetic alphabet will help you understand the relationship between sounds and letters, and thereby help you to become a better speller.

On page 248 and the facing page there are two charts. The first one, entitled "Consonant Sounds and Their Common Spellings," summarizes twenty-four main consonant sounds of English, the symbols used to represent these sounds, and common ways of spelling them. The *symbol* for each consonant sound is written between a pair of slanted lines. For example, the symbol/k/ stands for the sound of the first letter in the word *kit,* as you can see by looking at the chart. The sound /k/ may also be spelled by the letters *c* (as in *cold*), *ck* (as in *lick*), or *k* (as in *like*).

The second chart, "Vowel Sounds and Their Common Spellings," shows the symbols for fourteen main vowel sounds and the vowel sound called a *schwa*. If you look at the vowel sound /ī/ on the chart, you will see the several patterns or ways in which this sound may be spelled. For example, in the word *line,* it is spelled with the letter *i* followed by a consonant (*n*), which, in turn, is followed by an *e*. (The letters **VCe,** standing for *vowel, consonant, e,* represent *one* of the ways or patterns in which the sound /ī/ may be written in English.) Other ways include *–igh* as in *high; –y* as in *try; –ie* as in *die.*

The spelling patterns reflected in these two charts should help to balance the irregularities in English spelling. The point is, that *despite* exceptions and seemingly illogical spellings, our spelling system exists as it does for good historical reasons, and is, on the whole, a predictable system.

LESSON 9

Spelling: Three Sounds of the Letter *x*

If you examine the chart "Consonant Sounds and Their Common Spellings" on page 248 of this book, you will notice that there is no phonetic symbol in the sound column for the letter *x*. This is because the letter *x* spells sounds that are named by other letters.

Pronounce the words in the three lists below, paying particular attention to the *sound* of the letter *x* in each word. Try to determine what sound it represents in each list.

1	*2*	*3*
tax	exhaust	obnoxious
flexible	exhibit	complexion
explicit	exasperate	crucifixion
exterminate	exotic	
excavate	exude	

The three sounds of the letter *x* are contained in the following guides.

● The letter *x* represents the sound /ks/ in the words in list *1*. This /ks/ sound occurs most commonly at the ends of words, and when the prefix *ex* is followed by the sounds /p/, /t/, and /k/.

● The letter *x* represents the sound /gz/ in the words in list *2*. This sound occurs most frequently when the prefix *ex* is followed by silent *h* or by a vowel.

● The letter *x* represents the sound /ksh/ in the words in list *3*.

Note: In addition to the three sounds given in the guides above, the letter *x* represents the sound /z/ in words that *begin* with *x* (*xylophone, xenophobe*). It also represents the sound /gsh/ in words like *luxurious.* These two sounds of *x* are, however, quite uncommon. The few words that contain them must simply be memorized.

EXERCISE A   Indicate the sound of the letter *x* in each word below by writing ks or gz or ksh in the blank. (Add 10 points for each correct answer.)

1. box ../..../....
2. expenditure ../..../....
3. auxiliary ../..../....
4. next ../..../....
5. exertion ../..../....

6. extend ../..../....
7. asphyxiate ../..../....
8. exhilarating ../..../....
9. anxious ../..../....
10. axis ../..../....

EXERCISE B   Use each of the words in Exercise A in a separate sentence that shows understanding of the word.

1. ....
2. ....
3. ....
4. ....
5. ....
6. ....
7. ....
8. ....
9. ....
10. ....

EXERCISE C   List five words in which the letter *x* has the sound /ks/; three words in which it has the sound /gz/; and two words in which it has the sound /ksh/. Use words other than those taught in this lesson. (Add 10 points for each correct choice.)

/ks/	/gz/	/ksh/
1.	....	....
2.	....	....
3.	....	
4.		
5.		

EXERCISE D   Be prepared to write from dictation all of the words taught in this lesson.

CHAPTER TWO

Standard Capital-Letter Usage

Now that you have refreshed your knowledge of grammar terms, you will find this knowledge useful in the study of English mechanics in Chapters Two, Three, and Four. When we speak of *mechanics* in relation to written English, we mean capitalization, punctuation, and spelling. These lessons in mechanics will serve as a review of things you were taught in other years. Because you will be expected to capitalize, punctuate, and spell accurately in all your writing, the study of these skills is placed early in the course, and the skills are reviewed frequently. Capitalization and punctuation are reviewed in the Cumulative Reviews in each chapter. A spelling lesson is included in Chapters One to Ten.

Capital letters are useful means of pointing out to the reader the special way in which you are using a word. If you write to a friend that you had a delicious dinner at The Steakhouse on Main Street, your friend knows that the name of the restaurant is The Steakhouse and the name of the street is Main Street. If, however, you do not capitalize these words (at the steakhouse on the main street), you are giving much less definite information. Your friend knows only that the restaurant is a steakhouse and that it is on the main thoroughfare of the town.

Custom in the use of capital letters may vary a little. The rules in this chapter reflect the practice of most writers today.

LESSON 10

Persons and Places

To understand how to use capitals, you must understand what the word *proper* means when it is applied to nouns and adjectives. A *proper noun* is the name of one specific person, place, thing, or idea. The opposite of a proper noun is a *common noun.* A common noun does not name one specific person, place, thing, or idea. It merely names the general class or group. *Carol,* a proper noun, is specific; whereas *girl,* a common noun, merely names a class or group to which *Carol* belongs. A *proper adjective* is an adjective formed from a proper noun.

PROPER NOUNS	Antonia Brico	North Dakota	Oldsmobile	Christianity
COMMON NOUNS	conductor	state	car	religion

PROPER NOUNS	America	China	Sweden
PROPER ADJECTIVES	American flag	Chinese diplomacy	Swedish furniture

29

Note: Words which name a kind or a type (*hound, yawl, sedan*) are not capitalized. Names given to particular individuals within the type are proper nouns and are capitalized (*Fido, Seaspray* [yawl], *Buick*).

The kinds of proper nouns are covered by the rules in this chapter.

Capitalize the names of persons and capitalize personal titles preceding the name.

EXAMPLES   Andrew MacDonald   Martha Graham   General Crawford
               Professor Ortiz   Superintendent Jones   Mayor Gibson

Personal titles used alone or following a person's name may or may not be capitalized, depending upon the importance of the person's position and whether you are emphasizing the position.

EXAMPLES   Rose Kovacs, president of the Science Club
               Thomas Jefferson, Secretary of State
               the Governor, the Senator

The word *president,* when used to refer to the head of a nation, is always capitalized. Titles of high government officials are usually capitalized.

In general, words of family relationship (mother, father, etc.) are capitalized except when preceded by a possessive.[1] An exception to this statement is an expression such as "my Uncle Bill." Here we capitalize "uncle" even though it is preceded by the possessive pronoun *my.*

EXAMPLES   I met Mother at her office.
               I met my mother at her office.   (preceded by a possessive)
               Jane's father is president of the Rotary Club.   (preceded by a possessive)

Capitalize geographical names.

EXAMPLES   Grove City   Essex County   Long Island
               Atlantic Ocean   Green Pond   Ohio River
               White Mountains   Wilson State Park   Mohawk Valley
               Gardiner's Bay   International Falls   Twenty-third Street

The most frequent error in capitalizing geographical names is the failure to capitalize the noun which tells the nature of the thing named: street, lake, river, mountain, park, county, etc. As you can see from the examples above, these words are part of the whole proper name and are capitalized.

Note: Do not capitalize *east, west, north,* and *south* when they indicate directions. *Do* capitalize them when they refer to recognized sections of the country or areas of the world.

EXAMPLES   Our farm is one mile south of town.   (direction)
               We prefer the South for our winter vacation.   (section of country)

[1] In capitalization of *mother, father,* etc., when they are *not* preceded by a possessive, usage is sufficiently varied so that writing the words with a small letter cannot be considered incorrect. Acceptable: I met *mother* at her office. Preferable: I met *Mother* at her office.

30

EXERCISE A Insert capitals in the following items wherever they are required. (Add 4 points for each correct item.)

1. the hudson river
2. dorothea dix
3. secretary of defense
4. east of new york
5. lupe santos, captain of the team
6. mayor osaka
7. captain stanhope
8. president of the united states
9. uncle george
10. the middle west
11. the ozark mountains
12. olga muñoz, our club president
13. my mother
14. mackinac island
15. indian ocean
16. thirty-first street
17. montauk state park
18. a police lieutenant
19. industries in the south
20. young african nations
21. the north side of main street
22. the president of the student body
23. the republic of indonesia
24. stratford avenue
25. the governor of illinois

EXERCISE B Insert capital letters wherever they are required in the following sentences. Circle all capitals which should be small letters. (Add 10 points for each correctly marked sentence.)

1. From the klamath mountains at its Northern border to the burning mohave desert in the south, california is a land of contrasts.

2. Because my Mother did not know our family tree, I obtained information from uncle Frank, who knew all the branches, including the one in new england, the one in the south, and the one in the southwest.

3. The fertile willamette valley in oregon is bounded on the North by the columbia river, on the East by the cascade range, and on the West by the coast range.

4. As senator Smith explained, the work of a Senator is more interesting and less strenuous than that of a Governor.

5. The president called a meeting of the secretary of commerce and the secretary of labor in his white house office to listen to the lucidly expressed views of dr. Joyce James, Professor of economics at Yale university.

6. Below wilmington the delaware river broadens into delaware bay and, rounding cape may, new jersey, enters the atlantic ocean.

7. Someone told Bill's Father, who is a Policeman, about the accident at the corner of thirty-fourth street and third avenue, which sent two pedestrians to the hospital in critical condition.

8. I left a message for dr. Glenda Birch at the Drugstore on the west side of chestnut street opposite the entrance to Bliss park.

9. An american general conferred candidly in london with british officers about our european bases.

10. To reach boone lake in mountainside park, where the Seniors will hold their annual picnic, take the mohawk highway west for five miles and turn north on the road to bald mountain.

Organizations, Events, and Publications

Capitalize the names of organizations, institutions, business firms, and the brand names of business products, but not the word which denotes the nature of the product.

EXAMPLES   Stamp Club   Terrace Plaza Hotel
Northwestern High School   Broadway Theater
Adelphi College   General Electric Company
University of Vermont   Franklin Building
Congress   Kleenem toothpaste
Department of Agriculture   Ivory soap

Note: Words like *high school, college,* and *company* are not capitalized when used alone because when used alone they are not part of a proper name.

EXAMPLES   Although he did not finish high school, he enrolled at the university.
The company I work for makes electronic equipment.

Capitalize the names of special events, historical periods, and calendar items: days of the week, months, holidays, holy days.

EXAMPLES   Hofstra College Shakespeare Festival   Fourth of July
French Revolution   Labor Day
Middle Ages   Lincoln's Birthday

Capitalize the first word and all important words in the titles of books, newspapers, periodicals, articles, documents, laws, and works of art.

Giants in the Earth   Treaty of Versailles
The Bell Jar   Federal Reserve Act
the Saturday Review/World   The Man with the Hoe
the Wall Street Journal   "The Highwayman" (poem)

Note: The words *not* usually capitalized in a title are the articles (*a, an, the*) and short prepositions and conjunctions.

The words *a, an, the,* written before a title, are capitalized only when they are part of the title. Before the names of magazines and newspapers, they are not usually capitalized within a sentence.

EXAMPLE   After finishing *The Life of Frederick Douglass,* I read an article about it in the *Boston Globe.*

EXERCISE   Insert capitals in the following items wherever they are required. (Add 4 points for each correct item.)

1. a travel club
2. central high school
3. wilson college
4. the meadowbrook inn
5. a small college
6. the franklin theater
7. the university of hawaii
8. the department of commerce
9. the *evening globe*
10. memorial day
11. an uptown theater
12. *the ox-bow incident* (book)
13. the battle of gettysburg
14. *ebony* (magazine)
15. the middletown department store
16. zenith radios
17. the roosevelt hotel
18. beardsly shaving cream
19. cardiff castle
20. the american bill of rights
21. st. joseph's cathedral
22. the chrysler building
23. krispo piecrust mix
24. the prudential insurance company
25. the united nations security council

Indicate titles by underlining or by quotation marks.

In running text (within a sentence), underline titles of books, book-length poems, works of art (pictures, musical compositions, statues, etc.), and names of newspapers and magazines.

EXAMPLES   <u>Mutiny on the Bounty</u> (book)
<u>Paradise Lost</u> (book-length poem)
the <u>New York Times</u>
the <u>Scientific American</u>

Use quotation marks around titles of parts of publications (titles of chapters, magazine articles, poems, short stories, etc.).

EXAMPLES   To me, Marianne Moore's best poem is "The Steeple-Jack."

In "First Paydays," Chapter 10 of his autobiography, <u>Always the Young Strangers</u>, Carl Sandburg tells how hard he worked as a boy.

Note: If a comma or a period is used at the end of the quoted title, place it inside the closing quotation marks.

EXAMPLE   When you have read the story "Markheim," write a comment on it.

Note: The word *the* preceding the title of a newspaper or a magazine is not usually underlined in running text.

EXAMPLE   After I had read the <u>Boston Herald</u>, I turned to the <u>Atlantic Monthly</u>.

Note: Material which is underlined in a manuscript is italicized in print.

MANUSCRIPT   My book report is on Jane Austen's novel <u>Pride and Prejudice</u>.

PRINTED   My book report is on Jane Austen's novel *Pride and Prejudice*.

REVIEW EXERCISE

Insert capital letters wherever they are required in the following sentences. Circle all capitals which should be small letters. Indicate titles by inserting quotation marks or by underlining. (Add 10 points for each correctly marked sentence.)

1. On thursday, november 16, Rembrandt's painting, Aristotle contemplating the bust of Homer, was sold to the Metropolitan museum of art for $2,300,000 at the Parke-Bernet galleries at 980 Madison avenue in New York city.

2. At a meeting of the Dog Fancier's luncheon club at Lüchow's restaurant on fourteenth street, it was revealed that the american kennel club now lists the names of 1,990,850 purebred dogs.

3. Tickets for saturday's game for the championship of the ivy league will be on sale at John Hay hall on the Columbia university campus and at the Columbia university club, 4 West Forty-Third Street.

4. According to an article, government agents investigate local firm, in today's Springfield republican, the Miller drug company, distributor of dubious french perfumes, permo lipstick, hi-glo rouge, and curequick cold tablets, is being investigated by government agents.

5. Scutari, where Florence Nightingale labored tirelessly to improve military hospitals during the crimean war, is across the black sea from the crimean peninsula.

6. The two most famous statues in the Louvre in Paris are the Venus de Milo

and the Victory of Samothrace; the most famous painting is Leonardo da Vinci's Mona Lisa.

7. An appealing aspect of cornell university in ithaca, New York, is its beautiful location above lake cayuga, one of the famous finger lakes in the Central Part of the State.

8. When Mr. Ames, the huge football Coach at South high, has his big german shepherd dog beside him in his Morris Minor runabout, there's no room left for another passenger.

9. In the 1961 world series Roger Maris of the New York yankees became the first man to hit 61 home runs in one Season and was also voted the most valuable player in the American league.

10. In James Joyce's novel A Portrait of the artist as a young man, a famous scene is the nostalgically described christmas dinner which is almost wrecked by a quarrel over Politics and Religion.

Races, Nationalities, Religions

Capitalize the names of races, nationalities, religions.

EXAMPLES Caucasian   Italian   Roman Catholic   Judaism

Do not capitalize the names of school subjects, except languages and the titles of specific courses.

EXAMPLES Latin   English   Algebra II   Social Studies III
          algebra   social studies   chemistry   mathematics

Do not capitalize the names of the seasons.

EXAMPLES spring   fall   summer   winter

Capitalize words referring to the Deity.

EXAMPLES God   Father   Savior

The word *god* is not capitalized when it refers to the gods of ancient mythology. The names of particular gods within mythology, however, are capitalized, just as other proper nouns are.

Ask for the guidance of God, who understands your needs.
The Roman goddess of beauty was Venus.

EXERCISE Insert capital letters wherever they are required in the following sentences. Circle all capitals which should be small letters. (Add 5 points for each correct answer.)

1. We think of Midway Avenue as an avenue of churches because we find within three blocks a roman catholic church, an episcopal chapel, methodist, presbyterian, and baptist churches, and a jewish temple.

2. Heavy rains are needed this spring to enable our reservoirs to meet the demands of the hot weeks next summer and fall.

3. Although christians and jews worship the lord differently, faith in god is characteristic of both the christian and jewish religions.

4. Nationality is not the same as race; for example, a person whose nationality is american may be of the caucasian, negroid, or mongoloid race.

5. I learned my English grammar in latin class, american history in English III, and european history in french class.

REVIEW EXERCISE Insert capital letters wherever they are required in the following sentences. Circle all capitals which should be small letters. Insert quotation marks or underlining for titles. (Add 10 points for each correctly marked sentence.)

1. In english history the reformation, which was a european movement to bring about religious reforms, should not be confused with the restoration, which was the restoration of Monarchy in england, following the period known as the commonwealth, when england had no King.

2. The Summer following her graduation from College Lena spent studying writing at a university in the middle west, where she was encouraged by a professor of english to pursue writing as a career.

3. On may 29, 1910, Glenn H. Curtiss, an american pioneer in aviation, won a $10,000 prize offered by the New York world for the first continuous flight from albany to New York city.

4. Yorkminster, the massive cathedral built in the middle ages in the english city of York near the border of scotland, was characterized in its early years as one-half fortress against the scots and one-half monument to the glory of god.

5. The gulf stream, which is a kind of river in the Atlantic ocean, moves Northeastward from the gulf of Mexico to a point off the eastern coast of Newfoundland in the north Atlantic.

6. Some of the last areas of the World to be explored were the land masses near the south pole, the floating ice fields near the north pole, parts of Australia, some Pacific islands, the Himalayan mountains, and remote parts of the Amazon river in south America.

7. The mailing address of the publisher of the popular magazines, People, Time, and sports illustrated, is Time, Inc., Time and Life building, Rockefeller center, New York, New York 10020; the publisher of the Ladies Home Journal and Holiday is the Curtis Publishing company, 641 Lexington avenue, New York, New York 10022.

8. Splendid reproductions of Millet's painting the Angelus and Montagna's The crucifixion may be found in a back issue of Life.

9. Advanced art classes are permitted to leave the building to do sketching in fairgrove park, just across Monmouth boulevard from the high school, and in Riverside park on the East bank of grand river.

10. Short poems like Mari Evans' if there be sorrow and Dickinson's To Make a Prairie mean more to me than long, book-length poems like Masefield's the everlasting mercy and Robinson's Tristram.

Chapter Review

EXERCISE At the right, place the letter *A* or *B* to indicate which column contains the correctly capitalized expression. (Add 4 points for each correct answer.)

	A	B	
1.	Gloria Steinem, editor	Gloria Steinem, Editor	. . . .
2.	a mayor's responsibilities	a Mayor's responsibilities	. . . .
3.	Dunne, the former Governor	Dunne, the former governor	. . . .
4.	Ask your Mother.	Ask your mother.	. . . .
5.	on Forty-fourth Street	on Forty-Fourth Street	. . . .

6. a tour of the West   a tour of the west   . . . .

7. a navaho village   a Navaho village   . . . .

8. our local high school   our local High School   . . . .

9. the Edens expressway   the Edens Expressway   . . . .

10. Grofast hair restorer   Grofast Hair Restorer   . . . .

11. the Marie Curie Club   the Marie Curie club   . . . .

12. the Bankers Trust Company   the Bankers Trust company   . . . .

13. a Ford Agency   a Ford agency   . . . .

14. the Battle of Leyte Gulf   the battle of Leyte Gulf   . . . .

15. St. Valentine's day   St. Valentine's Day   . . . .

16. the French Revolution   the French revolution   . . . .

17. Montrose County Fair   Montrose county fair   . . . .

18. *Mutiny on the Bounty*   *Mutiny On The Bounty*   . . . .

19. my Algebra assignment   my algebra assignment   . . . .

20. spring sports   Spring sports   . . . .

21. god's blessing   God's blessing   . . . .

22. They worship many Gods.   They worship many gods.   . . . .

23. in english class   in English class   . . . .

24. Tina Morales, the director   Tina Morales, the Director   . . . .

25. Kay's Beauty Salon   Kay's Beauty salon   . . . .

LESSON 14

Cumulative Review

A   Write the part of speech above each italicized word, using the customary abbreviations. (Add 5 points for each correct answer.)

1   When *you* come to a *stop* sign, *bring* your car to a *complete stop*.

2   *Because* I did not *stop completely* at the *intersection near* school, Sergeant

3   Fisk, *who* is usually on *duty* there, *kindly* offered me *this* good advice and

4   *handed* me a *blue* slip of paper. *This* was a cordial invitation to meet

5   Judge Wilbur in Traffic Court on Friday, the thirteenth. *When* I accepted

6   the invitation, the judge *fined me* five dollars.

B The phrases and subordinate clauses in this exercise are numbered and italicized. In the correspondingly numbered spaces below, tell (a) if the word group is a phrase or a clause; and (b) what kind of phrase (adjective, adverb, participial, gerund, infinitive) or clause (adjective, adverb, noun) it is. (Add 2½ points for each correct answer.)

a. (1) *In the summer* our high school offers courses (2) *which are not offered* (3) *during the school year.*

b. (4) *Intercepting a long pass,* Bob raced (5) *toward the goal.*

c. (6) *When I was younger,* my favorite hobby was (7) *building model airplanes.*

d. (8) *Working late,* the stage crew managed (9) *to complete the set* (10) *before curtain time.*

e. (11) *If you like mysteries,* you will enjoy (12) *reading Poe's stories.*

f. The people (13) *in the back row* could not hear (14) *what the speaker said.*

g. The driver (15) *of the car* asked (16) *where we were going.*

h. After (17) *taking the bar exam,* Melinda worked (18) *for a judge* (19) *until she received the news* (20) *that she had passed the test.*

1 (a)............ (b)............ 11 (a)............ (b)............

2 (a)............ (b)............ 12 (a)............ (b)............

3 (a)............ (b)............ 13 (a)............ (b)............

4 (a)............ (b)............ 14 (a)............ (b)............

5 (a)............ (b)............ 15 (a)............ (b)............

6 (a)............ (b)............ 16 (a)............ (b)............

7 (a)............ (b)............ 17 (a)............ (b)............

8 (a)............ (b)............ 18 (a)............ (b)............

9 (a)............ (b)............ 19 (a)............ (b)............

10 (a)............ (b)............ 20 (a)............ (b)............

LESSON 15

Building Vocabulary

adamant /ád ə mant/, *n.* A legendary stone of the ancients, so hard it could not be penetrated.—*adj.*: Unyielding; hard. *Adamant* is used principally as an adjective: *We pleaded, but she remained adamant (unyielding).*

amenable /ə mḗ nə bə-l/, *adj.* Easy to persuade; open to suggestion; agreeable: *Tom will never give in an inch, but his brother will be amenable to our request. If the public is amenable to the law, enforcement will not be necessary.*

augment /aug mént/, *v.* To increase; to enlarge: *She augments her income by working overtime at night.*

chronic /krón ik/, *adj.* Constant; habitual;

39

with reference to a disease, long lasting: *We groaned when the teacher called on Steve because we knew him to be a chronic complainer. Al is a chronic sufferer from hay fever.* Chronic is derived from the Greek word *chronos,* which means *time.* Several common English words employ this root. A *chronometer* is a very accurate timepiece. A *chronology* is a list of events arranged in time order—the order of occurrence. *Chronological* means in order of time—*chronological order.*

cursory /kúr sər ē/, *adj.* Rapidly or hurriedly done: *Having given the chapter only a cursory reading, I was not prepared for the test.* Cursory suggests a superficial performance: *The experts had time for only a cursory examination, but they believed the painting to be genuine.*

eccentric /ek sén trik/, *adj.* Different from the usual; odd; peculiar: *The customs of foreigners seem eccentric to us, and our customs seem eccentric to foreigners.*—**eccentricity,** *n. Samuel Johnson's most amusing eccentricity was his habit of talking to himself.*

irrelevant /i rél ə vənt/, *adj.* Off the subject; not applicable: *In her essay on mountain climbing, Dena's discussion of trout fishing was irrelevant.*

lethargy /leth ər jē/, *n.* A state of inaction or indifference; dislike of activity: *A pronounced effect of undernourishment is the lethargy which it imposes on its victims.* —**lethargic** /li thár jik/, *adj. The actor's lethargic performance was due to illness.*

panacea /pán ə sē ə/, *n.* A cure-all; a general remedy for all ailments: *The President warned against expecting to find a panacea for the country's ills; each problem has its own solution.*

plebeian /pli bḗ ən/, *adj.* Common, unrefined. The common people of ancient Rome were called *plebs* in contrast to the aristocrats, who were called *patricians.* From *plebs* comes the word *plebeian,* meaning "like the plebs or commoners." *The aristocracy of Edinburgh considered Burns's plebeian manners highly amusing.*

EXERCISE Draw a line through the italicized words in the following sentences and write above them the one word in this lesson which will give the same meaning as the word or word group you crossed out. This is a test of your knowledge of the words in the lesson; it does not imply that the crossed-out expressions are necessarily faulty. (Add 5 points for each correct answer.)

1. The supply of food has been *increased* by the use of fertilizer, but we must not look on fertilizer as a *cure-all* for agricultural ills.

2. His *constant* indolence and *dislike of activity* can lead only to failure.

3. A *hurried* examination of the living room showed that my hosts had rather *commonplace* taste.

4. It is one of my grandmother's *peculiarities* that she has remained *unyielding* in her refusal to install a telephone.

5. Mr. Brown's private life is *unrelated to the matter,* provided he is *agreeable* to our regulations and not a *habitual* absentee.

6. On most financial matters the boss is *unyielding,* and yet when the employees wished to *add to* their pensions from company funds, she was surprisingly *easy to persuade.*

7. Janet's *peculiar* behavior was the natural result of her *dislike of activity.*

8. Miss Jean Brodie thought her teaching was a *cure-all* for the habits that are *typical of the common people.*

9. Our discussion became cluttered with details which were *off the subject,* and our real problems received only *hurried and superficial* attention.

REVIEW EXERCISE After each number, write the letter of the word which is closest in meaning to the word in italics. (Add 10 points for each correct answer.)

1. commendable *abstinence*
   a. appetite   b. willingness   c. success   d. denial

1. ....

2. a *candid* remark
   a. frank   b. subtle   c. fallacious   d. lucid

2. ....

3. a *beneficent* offer
   a. selfish   b. large   c. casual   d. kindly

3. ....

4. *adamant* against change
   a. lofty   b. changeable   c. unyielding   d. cruel

4. ....

5. of *dubious* quality
   a. mediocre   b. poor   c. doubtful   d. high

5. ....

6. a *cursory* investigation
   a. ridiculous   b. superficial   c. honest   d. thorough

6. ....

7. *irrelevant* comment
   a. unwise   b. unconnected   c. dangerous   d. confusing

7. ....

8. *augment* the supply
   a. increase   b. insure   c. cut off   d. lessen

8. ....

9. *eccentric* mannerisms
   a. disturbing   b. plebeian   c. peculiar   d. ill-bred

9. ....

10. disgraceful *indolence*
    a. carelessness   b. lethargy   c. failure   d. conduct

10. ....

LESSON 16

Spelling: Greek Word Parts

Hundreds of English words are derived from Greek words or word parts. Often such words contain letters or combinations of letters that may cause spelling problems.

A knowledge of the spelling and meaning of some common but difficult Greek word parts will help you to expand your vocabulary and to improve your spelling.

Try to master the meaning and spelling of the Greek word parts which follow. Memorizing the example words may prove helpful.

archy	rule of or by	mon**archy**
chron	time	**chron**ology
eu	good, pleasant	**eu**phoria
logy	study of, science of	geo**logy**
onym	name	syn**onym**
pathy	feeling, suffering	sym**pathy**
philo, phile	love, love of	**philo**sophy, anglo**phile**
poly	many	**poly**technic
pseud, pseudo	false, fake	**pseud**onym
psych	mind	**psych**osis
syn, sym	together, with	**syn**chronize, **sym**phony
tele	far, distant	**tele**vision

EXERCISE A Make a word of each incomplete word by writing in the blank the Greek word part from the list above that means the same as the italicized word in the sentence. (Add 10 points for each correct answer.)

A. Entomo..*logy*.. is the *study* of insects.

1. With a .... scope, one can watch things that are *far* away.

2. A .... ometer is an instrument that measures *time*.

3. Something .... phonic has a *pleasant* sound.

4. A matri .... is a society in which women *rule*.

5. A .... iatrist is a doctor who treats the *mind*.

6. An anti .... is a *feeling* against something or someone.

7. Bio .... is the *study* of life.

8. An ant .... is an opposite *name* (word).

9. A biblio .... is one who has a *love* of books.

10. A .... gon is a figure having *many* sides.

EXERCISE B Add one of the Greek word parts taught in this lesson to each word or word part below. The new word that results should have the meaning given in parentheses. (Add 10 points for each correct answer.)

1. socio .... (study of human relationships)

2. a .... (without feeling)

3. olig .... (rule by the few)

4. .... thermometer (an apparatus for measuring the temperature of a distant point)

5. .... phemism (a pleasant way of stating an unpleasant fact)

6. .... oanalysis (analysis of the mind)

42

7. ....ic (continuing for a long time)

8. ....chrome (having many colors)

9. ailuro.......... (a lover of cats)

10. an..........ous (without a name; of unknown name)

EXERCISE C Write words containing each of the Greek word parts listed on page 42. Use words not taught in this lesson.

1.	6. ....
2.	7. ....
3.	8. ....
4.	9. ....
5.	10. ....

EXERCISE D Be prepared to write from dictation all of the words covered in this lesson.

Twenty Words *Pretest—study—retest.* (Add 5 points for each correctly spelled word.)

1. a cross	6. cal en dar	11. for ty	16. sin cere ly
2. am a teur	7. col lege	12. hu mor ous	17. tem per a ture
3. ap pear ance	8. crit i cize	13. li cense	18. to mor row
4. beg gar	9. eigh th	14. nick el	19. twelfth
5. be gin ning	10. fi nal ly	15. per haps	20. writ ing

CHAPTER THREE

Standard Punctuation Usage:
End Marks and Commas

Mastery of punctuation is necessary if you wish to write clearly and be sure you have communicated your meaning. Most of us know more about punctuation rules than we regularly demonstrate in our writing. The reason for this disparity is a failure to proofread written work. You should read over everything you write to make sure it is properly punctuated.

The exercises in this chapter, in which you must insert punctuation in prepared sentences, are proofreading exercises. The practice provided by these exercises will carry over into your own writing if you proofread your papers before handing them in.

LESSON 17

End Marks; Commas for Series

A statement is followed by a period.

EXAMPLES   The President spoke candidly at his last news conference.
Today's temperature ranged from 50.3° to 65.8°.

A question is followed by a question mark.

EXAMPLE   Where did you spend your vacation?

Note: Distinguish between a statement containing an indirect question and a sentence which asks a question.

STATEMENT   No one knows who is coming.
QUESTION   Do you know who is coming?

An exclamation is followed by an exclamation point.

EXAMPLES   What a lucky break you had!
How exciting!

Use commas to separate items in a series.

EXAMPLES   Lethargy, procrastination, and indolence assure failure.

Compositions must be written in ink, properly labeled, and handed in on time.

Note: Follow your teacher's instructions concerning the use of a comma before the *and* joining the last two items in a series. Usually the meaning of the sentence is clear without this comma, but occasionally the comma affects the meaning.

CLEAR WITHOUT COMMA   The list of premiums included electrical appliances, wristwatches and silverware.

COMMA AFFECTS MEANING   At the store I bought onions, a bag of potatoes, and hamburger for the picnic. (Without the comma before *and* we read "a bag of . . . hamburger.")

If all items in a series are joined by "and" or "or," do not use commas.

EXAMPLE   Ida Roberts was held in high esteem by labor and management and government.

Do not use a comma before the final adjective in a series if this adjective is thought of as part of the noun modified.

INCORRECT   He is a courteous, gentlemanly, beneficent, old man.
CORRECT   He is a courteous, gentlemanly, beneficent old man.

The adjectives in this sentence modify "old man," not just "man." The adjective *old* and the noun *man* are thus considered to be a unit—like one word.

Use a semicolon to separate items in a series if the items themselves contain commas.

EXAMPLE   The outstanding players were Mary Wrenn, the captain; Helen Blake, last year's captain; and Jill Mauro, the captain-elect.

EXERCISE   Insert end marks and commas wherever they are required in the following items. There should be eighteen complete sentences. The marks of punctuation already there are correct. (Add 2 points for each correct answer.)

1. What is crime It is an offense against the laws of the state, covering such actions as burglary arson forgery bribery counterfeiting and murder An act of violence is not a crime if it is committed in self-defense by accident or by a police officer in the act of stopping a crime

2. In the past ten years assault burglary and larceny have increased Illegal gambling has become a nationwide well-organized business In one year the betting on dice roulette and card games amounted to thirty million dollars Government investigations revealed that gamblers and criminals extend their influence from New York to Boston Providence Miami New Orleans Chicago and Las Vegas What a shameful picture the statistics revealed

3. What can be done to eliminate crime There is no panacea We must strengthen the forces aiding crime prevention: education religion wholesome recreation family and child guidance We must wipe out our slums improve the health of our citizens eliminate inequalities of opportunity and augment our police forces The friendless the weak and the chronic victims of prejudice are entitled to the same quality of justice as the rich the powerful and the well connected

4. Out of gambling and its illegal profits grow many criminal actions, such as bribery gang wars and murder Gambling criminals organize into powerful groups which threaten our security endanger our moral standards and cost us millions of dollars What can be done to curb the power of these criminal organizations Plenty New York State, for example, has enacted legislation legalizing off-track betting which guarantees an honest transaction for the bettor creates a source of revenue for the state and gives the illegal bookmakers serious competition.

Commas for Interrupters

Use commas to set off appositives with their modifiers.

An appositive is a noun or pronoun—often with modifiers—that follows another noun or pronoun to identify or explain it.

To "set off" an expression within a sentence requires two commas. To "set off" an expression at the beginning or at the end of a sentence requires only one comma.

EXAMPLES   These two figures of speech, the metaphor and the simile, are essential to an understanding of poetry.

Federal authorities are studying flood prevention, a pressing problem.

When an appositive is very closely related to the word it refers to, no comma is necessary.

EXAMPLES   My sister Nan is the eccentric member of my family.

The poem "The Rebel" was written by Mari Evans.

My friend Dorothy is older than my friend Mary.

Use commas to set off words in direct address.

EXAMPLES   Read to the class, Tina, exactly what you have written.

Ed, will you please refrain from talking in class?

I must disagree with you, my friend.

46

Use commas to set off parenthetical expressions.

The following are commonly used parenthetically: *I believe* (*think, hope,* etc.), *I am sure, on the contrary, on the other hand, after all, by the way, incidentally, of course, in my opinion, for example, however, nevertheless, to tell the truth.*

EXAMPLES   Jacqueline is, I believe, our most dependable player.

No one, on the other hand, has won so many matches as Beth.

In dates and addresses consisting of two or more parts, put a comma after each part.

(Do *not* put a comma between the state and the zip code.)

EXAMPLES   On April 1, 1976, we moved to the house at 14 Hiram Road, Augusta, Georgia 30904.

Write to me at 42 Park Place, Evanston, Illinois 60201, as soon as possible.

EXERCISE   Insert commas wherever they are required in the following sentences. (Add 10 points for each correctly marked sentence.)

1. When Greta Conway former treasurer of Stark Paper Company was appointed to the important post Assistant to the President she became a member of the Board of Directors.

2. *Gould's Millions* a biography of Jay Gould American railroad magnate is in my opinion a lively history of one of our "robber barons" men who amassed fortunes at the expense of others.

3. My brother Fred graduated from college on June 8 1976 and left the next day for Fort Benning Georgia to continue his military training.

4. Some writers on the other hand make their books too romantic something a realistic novelist Wharton for instance seldom does.

5. Class when you have finished this exercise, please complete your sentence structure exercise the one you began yesterday.

6. Address your inquiries listeners to Box 34 Chicago Illinois 60606 or write to us your favorite radio station for information about this free offer.

7. Her eccentric daughter Helen became a successful actress one who as I recall played several leading roles on Broadway.

8. A letter addressed to me at the Mutual Building 41 Evins Avenue Cleveland Ohio 44104 will receive prompt attention.

9. The poet Eliot was born in St. Louis Missouri in 1888, but because he became a British subject, he is usually classed as a British writer.

10. Loose thinking by the way almost always results in loose writing; loose writing on the other hand is not necessarily indicative of loose thinking.

Insert end marks and commas wherever they are required in the following sentences. (Add 10 points for each correctly marked sentence.)

1. Do you want to go to college If so, you have many kinds of colleges to consider: coed colleges noncoed colleges junior colleges four-year colleges small colleges and large universities.

2. For many high school graduates however military service secretarial school or work experience would be a better choice than college.

3. Should you go to your father's or your mother's college just to be amenable Since colleges change over the years, social life campus activities athletics and clubs may be different now.

4. The prestige of a college is irrelevant because contrary to what some students think it is no guarantee of status a large income and a place in *Who's Who.*

5. Is prestige usually transferred from the college to the student, or is it on the contrary transferred from the graduate to the college All famous successful alumni I believe enhance the reputation of their colleges.

6. Dr. Eugenia Ekhardt dean of admissions at Walner College believes you should choose the college which is right for you in terms of your goals abilities interests needs and personality.

7. If you are interested in specific subjects mathematics science or languages for example you should of course investigate the strength of the college in those subjects.

8. My sister Jane wants to go to Oberlin College Oberlin Ohio to major in music, but her friend Gail has chosen a state college for her work in special education.

9. Prospective college students are advised to learn to study effectively to build an extensive vocabulary to read widely and to write write write.

10. Look out Here come the College Boards The examinations usually required of college candidates are the Scholastic Aptitude Test the Achievement Tests in specific subjects and the Writing Sample an essay to be sent to the college.

LESSON 19

Building Vocabulary

affable /áf ə bə-l/, *adj.* Sociable, friendly, agreeable: *His affable manner is the secret of his popularity.*—**affability**, *n.* *Having expected her to be disagreeable to us, we were pleasantly surprised by her affability.*

avarice /áv ə ris/, *n.* Greediness; extreme desire for wealth: *His avarice was responsible for his cruelty to his employees and unfairness to his competitors.*—**avaricious** /áv ə rísh əs/, *adj.*

bigot /bíg ət/, *n.* A person stubbornly and intolerantly devoted to one set of ideas, one party, church, etc.: *Your inability to see any other point of view marks you as a bigot.*—**bigoted**, *adj.* *In political matters she has always been bigoted.*—**bigotry**, *n.* *Bigotry is often an obstacle to freedom.*

charlatan /shár lə̇ tən/, *n.* A person who pretends to have knowledge or ability; a quack; an impostor: *Several doctors declared the defendant's medical witness to be a charlatan.*

coherent /kō hír ənt/, *adj.* Sticking together, logically organized and consistent: *The speech was entertaining, but it was not coherent; the parts were not closely related.*—**coherence**, *n.* *Coherence is a quality of good writing.*

diffident /díf ə dənt/, *adj.* Shy; lacking in self-confidence: *The confidence of diffident children will be strengthened by giving them projects which they can successfully complete.*—**diffidence**, *n.* *His diffidence is a severe social handicap.*

feasible /fḗ zə bə-l/, *adj.* Capable of being done; practicable: *Engineers declared the bridge project to be technically feasible.*

loquacious /lō kwắ shəs/, *adj.* Talkative; enjoys talking: *Being loquacious, Rita gave a long account of her experiences.*

pertinent /púr tə nənt/, *adj.* Relating directly to the subject: *In a decision on a costly project, the size of your treasury is pertinent information.* Antonym: *irrelevant.*

veracity /və rás ə tē/, *n.* Truthfulness: *He is an honest man; his veracity is beyond question.*—**veracious** /və rắ shəs/, *adj.*

EXERCISE In the blank at the right of each line, write a synonym—one word or a phrase—of the italicized word. Naturally you should attempt this exercise without looking back at the preceding definitions. Look back only when you find you cannot remember the meaning of a word. (Add 10 points for each correct answer.)

1. an *avaricious* collector   . . . .

2. a shameless *charlatan*   . . . .

3. a paragraph which is *coherent*   . . . .

4. a *loquacious* old man   . . . .

5. a remark which is *pertinent*   . . . .

6. praiseworthy *veracity*   . . . .

7. a *feasible* plan   . . . .

8. a *diffident* student   . . . .

9. an *affable* personality   . . . .

10. The man is a *bigot*.   . . . .

REVIEW EXERCISE Fill each numbered blank in the passage below with the word from the following list that makes the best sense in the context. Use each word only once. (Add 5 points for each correct answer.)

abstained	coerce	irrelevant
avarice	coherent	loquacious
beneficent	diffident	lucid
candid	dubious	pertinent
charlatan	indolent	veracity

On the third day of the trial the defense called its witnesses. The first proved to be so (1)..................... that he told almost too much. The second, on the other hand, was so (2)..................... before the large crowd that the lawyer had difficulty getting any answers at all from him. Jake Sparton, a self-styled inventor, whom reputable scientists consider a(n) (3).................., then gave his testimony, which was of (4)..................... value, his reputation for (5)..................... being slight. Furthermore, since Jake had never done a real day's work, everyone considered him a(n) (6)..................... person. The testimony of Molly Parsons, however, was uncluttered by (7)..................... information and muddy thinking. On the contrary, it was (8)..................... to the case and (9)..................... enough to be understood. It was organized in a(n) (10)..................... way. An honest person, she gave her (11)..................... opinions briefly, and she nobly (12)..................... from gossip, which she disliked. It was finally established that the defendant, although his wealth was the result of his (13)..................., and although he had never been known for any (14)................... action toward his neighbors, still was not the kind to (15)..................... another person into committing a robbery.

After each number, write the letter of the word which is *opposite* in meaning to the word in italics.

16. finally *coerced*
    a. considered   b. forced   c. persuaded   d. caught   16. ....

17. *chronic* failure
    a. complete   b. rare   c. timely   d. continual   17. ....

18. an obvious *fallacy*
    a. truth   b. collapse   c. argument   d. error   18. ....

19. *affable* disposition
    a. disagreeable   b. lethargic   c. friendly   d. sentimental   19. ....

20. *bigoted* attitude
    a. generous   b. narrow   c. broad-minded   d. selfish   20. ....

Commas for Nonessential Modifiers

The Nonessential Clause A nonessential clause is a subordinate clause which does not restrict or limit the meaning of the word it modifies. It merely adds an idea to the sentence.[1]

NONESSENTIAL   Anna Chin, who paid cash, received a discount.

In this sentence the subordinate clause *who paid cash* is not necessary to our understanding of who it was that received a discount. We know, without the clause, that it was Anna Chin. Since the clause is not essential to the meaning of the sentence, it is called *nonessential*. It is set off by commas.

Clauses and phrases modifying a proper name are almost always nonessential.

The Essential Clause The opposite of a nonessential clause is an essential clause, which does limit the meaning of the word it modifies. It is not set off by commas.

ESSENTIAL   All customers who paid cash received a discount.

In this sentence the clause *who paid cash* does restrict or limit the meaning of *customers,* the word it modifies. It was only those customers who paid cash who received a discount. In this use the clause is essential, restrictive, and should not be set off by commas.

Nonessential and Essential Phrases Phrases may also be used both nonessentially and essentially.

NONESSENTIAL   Our fullback, playing in today's game, broke his ankle.

In this sentence the phrase *playing in today's game* is not necessary to tell who broke his ankle. We know already that it was the fullback. The phrase is nonessential and is set off by commas.

ESSENTIAL   Students playing in today's game are excused from afternoon classes.

In this sentence the phrase *playing in today's game* is necessary to make clear who will be excused from afternoon classes—only those who are playing. The phrase is essential, restrictive, and is *not* set off by commas.

EXERCISE   Some of the italicized clauses and phrases in the following sentences are nonessential; some are essential. In the space at the right, write *N* if the expression is nonessential; write *E* if it is essential. Then insert commas to set off the nonessential expressions. (Add 5 points for each correctly marked sentence.)

1. Two composers *that I like* are Gershwin and Joplin.   . . . .

2. Students *who make the honor roll* receive special privileges.   . . . .

---

[1] Nonessential clauses are also called nonrestrictive; essential clauses are also called restrictive.

3. I called on Mayor Young *who knows all about village affairs.* . . . .

4. Mayor Young said that any person *who claims to know all about village affairs* is a charlatan. . . . .

5. The fourth year of English *which is required in this state* varies widely in content from school to school. . . . .

6. Why do college students *who are eighteen* seem more mature than high school students of the same age? . . . .

7. Golda Meir *while speaking to the press* gave several pertinent examples. . . . .

8. Send all examinations *which have not been graded* to the head of the department. . . . .

9. Starchy foods *which are almost always fattening* should be avoided by the overweight person. . . . .

10. Irma's determination *which some people consider stubbornness* makes her a strong competitor. . . . .

11. The man *who wears four gold stripes on his sleeve* is the captain. . . . .

12. This book *written by an experienced airline pilot* tells of the hazards of flying before commercial aviation was feasible. . . . .

13. Ida Tarbell's book will fascinate anyone *who reads it.* . . . .

14. My mother *desiring to return to work* enrolled in courses in her field. . . . .

15. Students *wishing to be excused from classes* must submit a written excuse. . . . .

16. The mechanic *acting on a hunch* inspected our tires and found a dangerous slash in one of them. . . . .

17. The Geneva meeting *which began on July 5* has been in session for nearly two months. . . . .

18. Students *who are chronically late* should be suspended. . . . .

19. The President's Cabinet *which consists of appointed members* both informs and advises the President. . . . .

20. The chess set *that you once owned* now belongs to my avaricious brother. . . . .

Change end marks and insert commas wherever they are required in the following passage. (Add 4 points for each correctly marked line.)

HEAVENLY WEATHER

1 Your local weather forecaster who is technically a meteorologist is a

2 highly trained hard-working scientific expert a specialist who can tell

3 you many things besides tomorrow's weather. Do you want to know

4 what the weather is like on the planet Jupiter. Ask your meteorologist.

5 Are you planning a trip to Mars. The meteorologists I am afraid will

6 have discouraging information for you. Those people who are constantly

7 studying temperatures air pressures wind movements and warm and cold

8 fronts in our own atmosphere become curious naturally about the

9 atmosphere on other planets. In this pleasant work they cannot moreover

10 be maligned by hunters picnickers travelers and farmers people who

11 usually rely on their forecasts. The public which is notoriously fickle

12 frequently changes its opinion of meteorologists praising them when their

13 forecasts prove correct maligning their dubious veracity when they prove

14 incorrect. The public cannot however challenge scientific statements

15 about worlds which are millions of miles away. Well what about the

16 weather on Jupiter. Jupiter we are told has a dense atmosphere of

17 methane and ammonia gas. What a smelly planet. The surface tempera-

18 ture of Mars which some astronomers have believed to be inhabited

19 is according to our meteorologist on the chilly side. The atmosphere of

20 Mars furthermore contains little oxygen or water giving it clear weather

21 but making it unsuitable to our kind of life. A spacesuit an oxygen tank

22 and a good supply of food water and heat will I am sure make your

23 planetary travels more comfortable. Remember space travelers that you

24 will have to contend with the state of weightlessness which is caused

25 as you know by the decrease in the pull of gravity.

Commas for Compound Sentences;
Introductory Expressions

Use a comma before <u>and</u>, <u>but</u>, <u>or</u>, <u>nor</u>, <u>for</u>, <u>yet</u> when they join two independent clauses, unless the clauses are very short.

EXAMPLES At the piano Lilly struck a chord, and the quartet repeated it.
Stay close to the west bank, or the current will catch you.
The motor stalled and we couldn't start it. (clauses too short to require separation by a comma; meaning clear)

Be sure to place the comma before, not after, the conjunction.

INCORRECT The play pleased everyone but, the seniors were enthusiastic.
CORRECT   The play pleased everyone, but the seniors were enthusiastic.

When the conjunction joins two verbs, not two sentences, a comma is incorrect.

EXAMPLES I finally called Al's home and learned where to find him. (no comma
before *and* because the *and* joins two verbs, *called* and *learned*)
I finally called Al's home, and his sister told me where to find him.
(comma before *and* because *and* joins two independent clauses)

Use a comma after an introductory adverb clause, an introductory participial phrase, or a succession of introductory prepositional phrases.

A group of words is introductory when it appears first in the sentence and qualifies the meaning of the ideas that follow it.

Introductory Adverb Clause

EXAMPLE After the crowd had left, the living room needed a thorough cleaning.

Introductory Participial Phrase

EXAMPLES Requiring little sun, this plant has flourished in my room.
Caught between their pursuers and the sea, the fugitives were forced
to surrender.

A Succession of Introductory Prepositional Phrases

EXAMPLE For a few days near the end of the term, we will review.

EXERCISE Insert commas wherever they are required in the following sentences.

54

In the space after each sentence, write the letter of the usage in the list below which explains the use of the comma. (Add 5 points for each correct sentence.)

    a. to separate independent clauses joined by *and, but, or, nor, for, yet*
    b. to set off an introductory adverb clause
    c. to set off an introductory participial phrase
    d. to set off a succession of introductory prepositional phrases

1. Built by plants and animals vitamins are organic compounds in our food supply.   . . . .

2. Although vitamins alone will not sustain health they are essential to the normal functioning of your body.   . . . .

3. With a knowledge of vitamins you will be able to plan your diet more carefully.   . . . .

4. Scientists have identified a large number of vitamins but researchers do not agree on the daily requirement of each.   . . . .

5. Since everyone's body chemistry, level of activity, and food intake varies average requirements may not be adequate for everyone.   . . . .

6. In the opinion of most nutrition experts a full and well-balanced diet should provide you with all the essential vitamins.   . . . .

7. If your diet is inadequate in any way you may need to take vitamin supplements in pill or liquid form.   . . . .

8. There are nine important vitamins and you should make sure to get adequate daily supplies of all of them.   . . . .

9. Without a sufficient supply of these vitamins you will lose energy and develop symptoms of illness.   . . . .

10. Found in carrots, sweet potatoes, egg yolks, and corn Vitamin A builds bones and teeth.   . . . .

11. For the prevention of night blindness Vitamin A is required.   . . . .

12. Of highest importance to growth and energy the Vitamin B-complex includes five key vitamins.   . . . .

13. Since the B vitamins are not stored in the body you must resupply the body with them every day.   . . . .

14. Eat whole-wheat products, liver, lean meat, nuts, and leafy vegetables for they will supply your Vitamin B needs.   . . . .

15. When Vitamin C is lacking the health of the gums is affected.   . . . .

16. The cells of the capillary walls weaken and blood leaks through the gums and other tissues.   . . . .

17. Formed by the action of the ultraviolet rays of the sun upon fatty

substances in the skin Vitamin D is found naturally in egg yolks, butter fat, and liver. . . . .

18. Vitamin D is vital for healthy bones and teeth but too large a daily intake may be dangerous. . . . .

19. Although experiments show that Vitamin E aids normal reproduction in some animals its function in the human body is not fully understood. . . . .

20. While there are indications that Vitamin E aids the healing of wounds this finding is not universally accepted. . . . .

Chapter Review

EXERCISE   Insert commas and change end marks wherever necessary in the following paragraphs. (Add 4 points for each correctly marked line.)

1   Have you ever seen a porpoise. If you have made the acquaintance
2   of any of these affable deep-sea clowns you have I am sure been amused
3   by their graceful swimming high spirits and grinning faces. What won-
4   derful actors they are. At aquariums along our coasts you will find
5   porpoises leaping several feet from the water to grab a proffered fish
6   playing tag with one another or nuzzling up to a diver who has invaded
7   their tank. Seen from ship or shore a school of porpoises provides a
8   delightful exhibition of speed grace and sheer playfulness.
9   It is not however the acting of the porpoise that has aroused scientific
10   interest. As a result of research scientists now believe that porpoises
11   communicate by means of a porpoise language. If the scientists are right
12   this language if that's what it is consists of whistles of varying tones.
13   One scientist a linguist and psychologist has picked out eighteen distinct
14   whistles. Is it possible that these whistles which no human being can
15   detect with the naked ear are actually words. The porpoise whistles and
16   other speech sounds were recorded during a six-month study at
17   Marineland on the Pacific Ocean in California.
18   Porpoises which are also called dolphins have large brains and biolo-

19 gists think the brain of a porpoise may be as complex as the human

20 brain.

21   The tones of the whistles which were recorded have been drawn

22 graphically and listed in order of frequency of occurrence. Although

23 some of these whistles may be used for navigation and food-finding

24 they may also be used as a kind of language. Can scientists learn to

25 speak this language.

Cumulative Review

A In the following paragraph, underline the subject of each sentence once and the verb twice. Circle the complements. Above each complement, write its name, using these abbreviations: *d.o.* (direct object), *i.o.* (indirect object), *p.n.* (predicate nominative), or *p.a.* (predicate adjective). (Add 10 points for each correctly marked sentence.)

1   The choice of a vocation concerns every senior. For many, the choice

2   is difficult. Guidance counselors give them pamphlets about vocations.

3   The advice of parents may not be helpful. Parents sometimes offer their

4   children a position in the family business. However, the family business

5   is not necessarily the right one for the young person. Another source

6   of help is the career conferences held at many schools. Facing four or

7   five years of college before going to work, many seniors are not able

8   to look so far ahead. Others simply do not have a strong interest in

9   any kind of work. The choice of a life work is indeed a perplexing

10 matter. Students must give it much thought.

B Insert capital letters and punctuation in the following sentences. (Add 4 points for each correct answer.)

1. Flo MacDonald president of the camera club is one of the girls who won prizes in the Eastman kodak company's contest.

2. During a tour of the west last summer my father whose hobby is photography took pictures in Yellowstone park with his pentax camera.

3. When you travel with a camera fiend you have to photograph every

waterfall big tree lake and wild animal you see. What a nuisance

4. I wish my marks in chemistry math and english were as good as my marks in photography a subject of little help in college entrance examinations.

5. At Monty's camera shop on the south side of Stratford avenue students at Gardner high school can get a 10 per cent discount.

6. What kind of camera do you want You can I'm sure find it at Monty's which carries german Japanese and american makes.

Building Vocabulary

altruism /ál trū íz əm/, n. Concern for others, their interests, welfare, etc.: *Unlike selfish people of wealth, he was noted for his altruism.* —altruistic /ál trū ís tik/, adj.: *Paying for her nephews' education was her most altruistic act.*

derogatory /di róg ə táur ē/, adj. Showing an unfavorable opinion of someone or something; belittling: *After reading many derogatory opinions of Charlotte Smith, we decided not to vote for her.*

dogmatic /daug mát ik/, adj. Speaking as though one's opinions were established fact; positive; overbearing: *When I hear his dogmatic statements, I always want to prove him wrong.*

emulate /ém yə lāt/, v. To imitate another person in order to equal or surpass the person: *A girl often emulates her older sister.* —emulation, n. *He applauded my emulation of José Feliciano.*

expedient /ik spē dē ənt/, adj. Useful for producing a desired result; advisable; advantageous: *There may be occasions when it will be more expedient for you to keep silent than to argue. An action may be expedient yet wrong; advantageous but not advisable. It may be expedient for you to charge gasoline to your parents' account, but it may not be right to do so.* —expedient, n. A means or a device for producing a desired result: *To avoid trouble, he chose the cowardly expedient of telling a lie.*

gregarious /gri gár ē əs/, adj. Living in a flock or herd; fond of associating with others: *A gregarious person is bored living alone.*

indigent /ín də jənt/, adj. Needy, poor: *The Red Cross keeps a list of the indigent families in the city.*

lucrative /lū krə tiv/, adj. Financially profitable: *Our annual village fair is a lucrative undertaking.*

obsolete /ób sə lēt/, adj. No longer in use; out-of-date: *As golfing apparel, knickerbockers are obsolete.*

opulence /óp yə ləns/, n. Wealth, riches, abundance as shown in luxurious living: *A visit to the rich woman's estate revealed her unbelievable opulence. Rockefeller's opulence was incalculable* —opulent, adj.

EXERCISE Write before each word the letter of its synonym on the right. (Add 10 points for each correct answer.)

.... 1. dogmatic

.... 2. emulate

.... 3. expedient

a. wealth

b. advantageous

c. positive

.... 4. gregarious   d. concern for others

.... 5. opulence   e. poor

.... 6. obsolete   f. imitate

.... 7. lucrative   g. belittling

.... 8. derogatory   h. out-of-date

.... 9. indigent   i. financially profitable

.... 10. altruism   j. fond of being with others

REVIEW EXERCISE Write the adjective form of each of the following nouns. (Add 4 points for each correct answer.)

A. beauty   *...beautiful...*

1. fallacy   ....   6. bigot   ....

2. nostalgia   ....   7. veracity   ....

3. abstinence   ....   8. altruism   ....

4. lethargy   ....   9. opulence   ....

5. avarice   ....   10. indolence   ....

Place in the space at the right the letter of the word which is closest in meaning to the italicized word.

11. *feasible* suggestion
   a. absurd   b. brilliant   c. practicable   d. helpful   11. ...

12. *obsolete* equipment
   a. superior   b. out-of-date   c. durable   d. new   12. ...

13. a possible *panacea*
   a. objection   b. loss   c. substitute   d. cure-all   13. ...

14. an *altruistic* offer
   a. unselfish   b. unacceptable   c. meager   d. pleasing   14. ...

15. an *indigent* author
   a. needy   b. insecure   c. established   d. annoyed   15. ...

16. *plebeian* taste
   a. cultivated   b. pleasing   c. unrefined   d. eccentric   16. ...

17. a *lucrative* job
   a. hard   b. well-paying   c. permanent   d. easy   17. ...

18. an *amenable* mood
   a. dogmatic   b. nostalgic   c. angry   d. agreeable   18. ...

19. a *dogmatic* manner
   a. well-bred   b. carefree   c. overbearing   d. sly   19. ...

20. careful *emulation*
    a. escape   b. planning   c. imitation   d. dictation 20. ...

21. a *beneficent* act
    a. sudden   b. thoughtless   c. cruel   d. helpful   21. ...

22. a *cursory* examination
    a. complete   b. superficial   c. detailed   d. thorough   22. ...

23. an *eccentric* personality
    a. lovable   b. disagreeable   c. charming   d. peculiar   23. ...

24. *lucid* writing
    a. clear   b. smooth   c. loose   d. lengthy   24. ...

25. *candid* confession
    a. shocking   b. short   c. straightforward d. reluctant 25. ...

Spelling: French Loan Words

There is a large group of French loan words that entered the English language in the nineteenth and twentieth centuries. Indeed, French loan words such as *discothèque* and *cinema verité* (as well as loan words from many other languages) are continuously being "borrowed" by us English-speaking people. These French loan words have usually retained their French pronunciation and spelling. They do not, therefore, follow English spelling patterns. You can both pronounce and spell many French loan words if you make yourself familiar with certain common sound-spelling patterns peculiar to the French language.

Learning the guides below will enable you to correctly pronounce and spell the French loan words that follow each guide, as well as the other similar French words.

● The sound /ō/ at the end of many French loan words is spelled *eau*. Say the following words aloud:

    bur**eau**   plat**eau**
    trouss**eau**   chat**eau**

● The sound /ā/ at the end of French words is sometimes spelled *é*. Say these words:

    blas**é**   clich**é**
    proteg**é**   consomm**é**

● A number of French loan words end in silent *t* or silent *s* after a long vowel. Say these words:

    bere**t**   apropo**s**
    fille**t**   debri**s**

● The sound /g/ (as in *pig*) at the end of many French loan words is often spelled *gue*. Say these words:

fati**gue**	collea**gue**
lea**gue**	mor**gue**

● The sound /œr/ is spelled *eur* at the end of many loan words. Say these:

chauff**eur**	connoiss**eur**
sabot**eur**	entrepren**eur**

EXERCISE A Indicate the sound of the italicized letter or letters in each word below by writing ō, ā, g, or œr between the slanted lines. If the italicized letter is silent, write *sil*. (Add 5 points for each correct answer.)

1. risqu*é*../..../....
2. rendezvou*s*../..../....
3. racont*eur*../..../....
4. chap*eau*../..../....
5. chale*t*../..../....
6. dialo*gue*../..../....
7. caf*é*../..../....
8. pass*é*../..../....
9. provocat*eur*../..../....
10. va*gue*../..../....

11. liqu*eur*../..../....
12. portmant*eau*../..../....
13. sache*t*../..../....
14. catalo*gue*../..../....
15. fianc*é*../..../....
16. tabl*eau*../..../....
17. balle*t*../..../....
18. saut*é*../..../....
19. pla*gue*../..../....
20. debu*t*../..../....

EXERCISE B Choose ten words from Exercise A and use each in a separate sentence that reveals its meaning.

1. ....
2. ....
3. ....
4. ....
5. ....
6. ....
7. ....
8. ....
9. ....
10. ....

EXERCISE C Be prepared to write from dictation all of the words taught in this lesson.

REVIEW EXERCISE Be prepared to write from dictation each of the following words. (Add 5 points for each correctly spelled word.)

1. synchronize
2. exhilarating
3. euphoria
4. pseudonym
5. exasperate

6. exuberant
7. obnoxious
8. chronology
9. luxurious
10. crucifixion

11. excavate
12. polygon
13. anxious
14. matriarchy
15. anglophile

16. psychosis
17. asphyxiate
18. anonymous
19. synthesis
20. explicit

CHAPTER FOUR

Standard Punctuation: Semicolon, Quotation Marks, Apostrophe

Although the semicolon is a valuable mark of punctuation, it should be used sparingly. Learn the few important ways the semicolon should be used, and then use it in those ways only. Quotation marks, which are used principally to set off the exact words of a person speaking, are so familiar that a brief review should be sufficient for you. The apostrophe is still an important mark of punctuation although many writers seem to find its correct use an insoluble mystery.

The correct use of the semicolon, like the correct use of the comma, is frequently a matter of the writer's judgment. Quotation marks and the apostrophe, however, are never matters of judgment; they always follow definite and inflexible rules.

LESSON 26

The Semicolon

Use the semicolon between independent clauses closely related in thought and not joined by <u>and</u>, <u>but</u>, <u>or</u>, <u>nor</u>, <u>for</u>, <u>yet</u>.

EXAMPLES　Sharks circle in the distance, watching the skin diver; as soon as the diver shoots a fish, they move in to share the kill.
Spear fishing is always interesting; it is frequently precarious.

Note: Semicolons are better than periods in these sentences because the clauses are so closely related in thought. Periods, however, would be technically correct.

Use a semicolon between independent clauses joined by <u>and</u>, <u>but</u>, <u>or</u>, <u>nor</u>, <u>for</u>, or <u>yet</u> if the clauses contain commas.

EXAMPLE　If you are contemplating a short vacation trip, you will do well to consider the bicycle; for it is a pleasant, healthful, and inexpensive means of transportation.

Use a semicolon between independent clauses joined by such words as:

accordingly	consequently	however	nevertheless	that is
also	for example	instead	otherwise	therefore
besides	furthermore	moreover	still	thus

63

Note: A period instead of a semicolon before these words is also correct.

When *for example, for instance, that is,* and *however* appear at the beginning of the second clause, they are followed by a comma. The other words in the list may or may not be followed by a comma, depending upon the taste of the writer.

EXAMPLES A single, highly developed skill may provide the margin of victory; for instance, a powerful serve in tennis will sometimes enable a player to win over a better all-around player.

Road repairs may cause traffic jams; nevertheless, some repairs must be made even during congested hours.

At first the manager refused to meet with the grievance committee, a group she had appointed; but, when she realized her mistake, she sent for Mr. Kowalsky, the head of the committee.

Note: Although a comma is the usual mark of punctuation between two independent clauses joined by *but* (Lesson 21), the semicolon is preferable in the last example above because there are commas within the joined sentences.

REVIEW EXERCISE Insert semicolons (not periods) and commas wherever they are required in the following sentences. (Add 10 points for each correctly marked sentence.)

1. Illustrations make a book attractive to young readers the pictures often help them to understand the book better.

2. Several factors affect one's choice of a vocation for instance environment parents' wishes and one's own work experiences are important influences.

3. As a scientific phenomenon the nuclear age began with the explosion at Los Alamos in 1945 in world relations however it really began about ten years later.

4. Newspaper editors must know what their readers are interested in for example tabloid editors will not devote their front pages to the same stories that will occupy the front page of the *New York Times*.

5. Warmongers are people who do not know what has happened in the last thirty years their concept of war is obsolete and they have not been able to realize what a nuclear war would be like.

6. According to the theory of natural selection, the stronger or more adaptive members of a species live longer and reproduce more the weaker and less adaptive ones perish without reproducing themselves.

7. Words in themselves are not dignified silly wise or malicious but they can be used in these ways by dignified silly wise or malicious people.

8. Our school band which has won several awards in the past will be sent to Riverdale for the music contest but the orchestra a relatively inexperienced group will not be sent this year.

9. The goal of science is to discover the truth about nature it cannot tolerate guesswork or unsupported conclusions.

10. True scientists are rightly intolerant of the guesswork of charlatans however they sometimes have to base their own research on hypotheses which are really mere guesses.

Quotation Marks

Use quotation marks to enclose a direct quotation—a person's exact words. Do not use quotation marks to enclose an indirect quotation—another's ideas expressed in your own words.

DIRECT QUOTATION   Marian said, "We'll leave at noon."
INDIRECT QUOTATION   Marian said that they would leave at noon.

1. A direct quotation begins with a capital letter.
2. A direct quotation is set off from the rest of the sentence by commas.

EXAMPLE   Mrs. Barry said, "Omit the first exercise."

If the quotation is only a phrase or fragment, it is not necessary to begin it with a capital or to set it off by commas.

EXAMPLE   A dotted line on the road map means "under construction."

3. Commas and periods are always placed inside the closing quotation marks.

EXAMPLE   "I'm finished," she declared.   She declared, "I'm finished."

4. Semicolons are placed outside the closing quotation marks.

EXAMPLE   Mr. James said, "You may have the entire period for this test"; however, he asked for our papers after twenty minutes.

5. Question marks and exclamation points are placed inside the closing quotation marks if they belong with the quotation; otherwise they are placed outside.

INCORRECT	"Where do you live," she inquired?
CORRECT	"Where do you live?" she inquired. (The quotation is a question.)
INCORRECT	"What an energetic woman," he exclaimed!
CORRECT	"What an energetic woman!" he exclaimed. (The quotation is an exclamation.)
CORRECT	Did you hear me say, "Please call for Jean"? (The entire sentence is a question; the quotation itself is not a question.)
CORRECT	How impolite of you to say, "I want a big helping"! (The entire sentence is an exclamation, not the quotation itself.)

6. When a quoted sentence is divided into two parts by such interrupting expressions as <u>he said</u>, <u>she replied</u>, <u>Jack added</u>, the second part begins with a small letter unless some other rule requires a capital.

EXAMPLES "You see," she added, "how plebeian your manners are."
"A mile from here the highway turns sharply to the right," she warned; "therefore drive slowly."

7. If the second part of an interrupted quotation is a new sentence, it begins with a capital letter. The preceding sentence must be followed by a period.

EXAMPLE "We will always have the struggle for power," he predicted. "Until war is no longer feasible, we shall have wars."

8. Use single quotation marks to enclose a quotation within a quotation.

EXAMPLES Tom said, "If you had only said, 'Marge is going to be there,' I'd have come sooner."
Carmen said, "Read my article, 'A Panacea for Lincoln High,' today."

9. When you write dialogue (two or more persons carrying on a conversation), begin a new paragraph every time the speaker changes.

"Is that you, George?" I called, peering under the tent flap.
"Yeah, it's me all right. What a night!" George was stumbling around somewhere in the woods.
"Wait a minute, George, until I find the flashlight." I reached for the light and clicked it on.

EXERCISE Insert punctuation and capital letters wherever required in the following sentences. (Add 10 points for each correctly marked sentence.)

1. Why can't I have my own private telephone she asked if I pay for it myself

2. Your remark is irrelevant exclaimed Ms. Carter surely you can do better than that

66

3. Jean said that she thought the invitation was for Sunday afternoon

4. Two good things about baby-sitting Arnold said are that it is lucrative and you can get a lot of homework done

5. Yes laughed Helen provided you can resist the temptation of television parents aren't around to check on you

6. Did the sign say turn right at the second traffic light Amelia asked

7. Quiet cried Mr. Boyd as he entered study hall everybody get to work

8. Your outline was full of technical errors Mr. Adams said nevertheless I gave you a good grade on the composition

9. Take your time he advised you'll do a better job

10. True altruism is a rare trait she said even in people who have been raised in opulent surroundings

LESSON 28

The Apostrophe

1. To form the possessive case of a singular noun, add an apostrophe and an s.

EXAMPLES   Bill's dog   child's book   Tess's skis

The exceptions to this rule are proper nouns of two or more syllables which end in *s*. To form the possessive case of such words, usually only an apostrophe is added.

EXAMPLES   Bontemps' poem   Frances' opinion

If you are in doubt about the possessive case of a proper noun ending in *s*, try to make what you write reflect what you say. In speaking, you say *Besses* car, not *Bess* car; hence, you write *Bess's*, not *Bess'*. Similarly, if you say *Francis* opinion rather than *Francises* opinion, you write *Francis'* rather than *Francis's*. If you say *Keatses* sonnet, you write *Keats's;* but if you say *Keats* sonnet, you write *Keats'*. Either form is acceptable.

The indefinite pronouns (*one, everyone, everybody,* etc.) form their possessive case in the same way as nouns.

EXAMPLE   Everybody's clothes were drenched.

2. To form the possessive case of a plural noun not ending in s, add an apostrophe and an s.

EXAMPLES   children's books   men's clothing

67

3. To form the possessive case of a plural noun ending in <u>s</u>, add the apostrophe only.

    EXAMPLES <u>girls'</u> opinions   the <u>Thompsons'</u> cottage

4. Personal pronouns in the possessive case (his, hers, its, ours, yours, theirs, whose) do not require an apostrophe.

    INCORRECT   Is this hat *your's*?
    CORRECT   Is this hat **yours**?
    INCORRECT   The house collapsed when *it's* foundation shifted.
    CORRECT   The house collapsed when **its** foundation shifted.

EXERCISE A   Fill the blanks in the first column with the singular possessive of the word at the left; fill the blanks in the second with the plural possessive. (Add 5 points for each correct answer.)

SINGULAR POSSESSIVE   PLURAL POSSESSIVE

A. customer *customer's* complaint B. *customers'* complaints

1. worker .... hammer 2. .... hammers

3. tree .... branches 4. .... branches

5. boy .... bicycle 6. .... bicycles

7. chair .... legs 8. .... legs

9. champion .... award 10. .... awards

11. woman .... handbag 12. .... handbags

13. helper .... wages 14. .... wages

15. adviser .... idea 16. .... ideas

17. friend .... advice 18. .... advice

19. dog .... collar 20. .... collars

5. In compound (hyphenated) words, names of business firms, and words showing joint possession, only the last word is possessive in form.

    COMPOUND WORD   brother-in-law's car
    BUSINESS FIRM   Lewis and Conger's annual sale
    JOINT POSSESSION   Laura and Bill's canoe
    INDIVIDUAL POSSESSION Laura's and Bill's canoes

6. When used as possessives, the words <u>minute</u>, <u>hour</u>, <u>day</u>, <u>week</u>, <u>month</u>, <u>year</u>, etc., require an apostrophe. Words indicating amount in cents or dollars, when used as possessives, require an apostrophe.

68

	Singular Possessive	Plural Possessive
EXAMPLES	an hour's work	two hours' work
	one dollar's worth	five dollars' worth

EXERCISE B In the following expressions possession is shown by a phrase which may be replaced by a noun in the possessive case. In the blank following each expression, write correctly the possessive form of the italicized noun or nouns. (Add 10 points for each correct answer.)

A. book of the *teacher*	*teacher's*	book
1. veracity of the *witness*	....	veracity
2. notebooks of *Sue and Barbara*	....	notebooks
3. father of my *sister-in-law*	....	father
4. weight of *it*	....	weight
5. toys of the *babies*	....	toys
6. worth of *fifty cents*	....	worth
7. publications of *Simon and Schuster*	....	publications
8. room of *Father and Mother*	....	room
9. duties of the *sergeant-at-arms*	....	duties
10. poems of *Gwendolyn Brooks*	....	poems

EXERCISE C Insert an apostrophe in the correct place in each italicized word which requires an apostrophe. In the blank after each item, write *before* if an apostrophe should be placed before the final s in the italicized word, *after* if it should be placed after the s, and *omit* if no apostrophe is required. (Add 5 points for each correct item.)

1. The fault is *ours*.	....	7. this *years* crops	....
2. a *days* journey	....	8. three *years* duration	....
3. *mens* shoes	....	9. Is it *yours*?	....
4. *countries* imports	....	10. a *bigots* opinion	....
5. an *hours* fun	....	11. a *captains* signal	....
6. *students* athletic field	....	12. the *horses* tails	....

13. *mail carriers* routes .... 17. the *Whites* cottage ....

14. both *partners* errors .... 18. Was it *theirs?* ....

15. a *girls* school .... 19. *everyones* attention ....

16. the *Rockefellers* .... 20. a *quarters* worth ....
    wealth

7. Use an apostrophe to indicate where letters have been omitted in a contraction.

do not = don't   we will = we'll   where is = where's

it is = it's   does not = doesn't   Ian is coming = Ian's coming

Note: It's requires an apostrophe only when it is a contraction meaning *it is* (or *it has*). As a possessive, *its* does not have an apostrophe.

EXAMPLES   It's (It is) good to see you.

         The experiment proved its (possessive) value.

LESSON 29

Chapter Review

A   Insert capital letters, apostrophes, semicolons, quotation marks, and other necessary punctuation. (Add 10 points for each correctly marked sentence.)

1. Although the teen-agers parents hadnt been aware of their childrens misbehavior after school declared the judge this fact doesn't excuse the parents entirely for its the parents duty to know their childrens friends and activities

2. If you know its speed and path you can follow the satellite across the sky with the naked eye the night of course must be clear and preferably moonless

3. Youre certainly wrong she exclaimed dogmatically why cant you listen to reason

4. Whats your objection to Ginos plan she asked isnt it feasible

5. Mrs. Campbell was disappointed by her partys political platform nevertheless she found it expedient to vote a straight ticket as usual

6. Its possible that if Brutus speech had been as clever as Antonys the Romans reaction would have been different in other words theyd have supported the conspirators

7. Didnt James sister say shed pick you up after the dance Mother asked yes but her obsolete car broke down I explained and she couldnt let us know

8. If theres a panacea for that nations economic ills it is courageous expansion by private industry augmented production means more jobs

9. The United Nations successful resistance to aggression in various parts of the world shows its superiority over its predecessor the League of Nations

10. Ive memorized Christina Rossettis poem A Better Resurrection Jerry announced to his teachers astonishment wouldnt you like to hear me recite it

B In the blank following each expression, write the possessive form of the italicized noun. (Add 10 points for each correct answer.)

A. skill of the *players* ....*players'*...... skill

1. office of my *daughter* .... office

2. car of *Shelley and Pete* .... car

3. house of the *Whitneys* .... house

4. deceptions of a *charlatan* .... deceptions

5. store of *Sherman and Fisk* .... store

6. room of the *children* .... room

7. delay of *two days* .... delay

8. leadership of *Addams* .... leadership

9. a paradise for *skiers* .... paradise

10. opinions of *others* .... opinions

LESSON 30

Cumulative Review

A The phrases and subordinate clauses in this exercise are numbered and italicized. In the correspondingly numbered spaces below, tell (a) whether the word group is a phrase or a clause, and (b) what kind of phrase (adjective, adverb, participial, gerund, infinitive) or clause (adjective, adverb, noun) it is. (Add 5 points for each correct answer.)

(1) *Like many other things nowadays,* the material (2) *that makes up the human body* has risen steeply in price. Dr. Donald T. Forman, (3) *who is a biochemist at Northwestern University,* estimated (4) *that the inorganic components of a person weighing one hundred and fifty pounds are now worth about $5.60.* Their worth, (5) *calculated in dollars and cents,* was estimated (6) *to be 98 cents* (7) *in 1939* and $3.50 in 1969. (8) *Because more than 60 percent of body weight is water and a third is fat and protein,* ash and minerals make up only 5.7 percent of body weight. (9) *Learning our monetary value,* (10) *even at inflated prices,* is a humbling discovery.

1 (a). . . . . (b). . . . .   6 (a). . . . . (b). . . . .

2 (a). . . . . (b). . . . .   7 (a). . . . . (b). . . . .

3 (a). . . . . (b). . . . .   8 (a). . . . . (b). . . . .

4 (a). . . . . (b). . . . .   9 (a). . . . . (b). . . . .

5 (a). . . . . (b). . . . .   10 (a). . . . . (b). . . . .

B Insert punctuation and capital letters in the following passage. Change incorrect punctuation. (Add 5 points for each correct answer.)

1   Dr. Fred C. Iklé the director of the arms control and disarmament
2   agency revealed that a nuclear war could destroy the ozone layer
3   in the stratosphere, this layer protects all living things from the suns
4   ultraviolet radiation. The potential depletion of the ozone layer by
5   nuclear explosions is an important new scientific discovery. Re-
6   searchers dont know exactly how much ozone depletion would result
7   from a large nuclear explosion. The depletion might be imperceptible
8   or its effects might be totally destructive. Ozone depletion may only
9   increase the hazards of sunburn however it might destroy critical links
10   in the food chain of plants and animals. Speaking candidly Dr. Iklé
11   said we do not know how long such effects would last. Since the
12   possible dangers of ozone depletion are so serious Dr. Iklé hopes
13   this discovery will lead to greater efforts toward nuclear disarmament.
14   If the planets food chain was damaged no nation would be able to
15   escape the consequences.

Building Vocabulary

lugubrious /lū gǘ brē əs/, *adj.* Sad, mournful: *She wore a lugubrious expression, as if she had lost her best friend.*

ostentatious /ós tən tā shəs/, *adj.* Showy; indicating fondness for unnecessary outward display: *In his opinion the man's clothes were ostentatious and showed bad taste.*

phlegmatic /fleg mát ik/, *adj.* Sluggish; calm; not easily aroused: *Freida's phlegmatic disposition is an advantage in a crisis. Father is too phlegmatic to be disturbed by children's quarrels.*

plausible /pláu zə bə-l/, *adj.* Seeming to be true and reasonable. A *plausible* argument is one which *sounds* convincing: *What you say is plausible enough, but I doubt that it is true. Since one of the damaged cars had a flat tire, a blowout was a plausible explanation of the accident.*

reactionary /rē ák shən ér ē/, *adj.* Favoring return to a former state of affairs, especially in politics: *Believing that the country is worse off today than it was twenty years ago, he joined the reactionary wing of his party.—n. Being a reactionary, she will vote with the conservatives.*

The Prefix in- The Latin prefix *in-* often means "not." You are familiar with many words which illustrate this point: *incomplete* (*not* complete); *indefinite* (*not* definite); *inadequate* (*not* adequate); and so on.

The remaining five words in this lesson begin with *in-* or *im-*, which is a form of *in-*. You will always find these words easier to understand if you substitute the word *not* for the prefix *in-*.

impunity /im py-ū nə tē/, *n.* Freedom from punishment. You will recognize from its root that *punity* is related to *punish*. *Im-* being, like *in-*, a negative prefix, when you act *with impunity*, you act *without punishment*: *In this coastal area nothing comes through a hurricane with impunity.*

incorrigible /in káur ə jə bə-l/, *adj.* Not capable of being corrected; not correctable. When people's bad habits are so firmly established that nothing but bad behavior can be expected of them, they are said to be *incorrigible*. The word is always used with reference to bad behavior. It would be an unusual use of the word to say that a person is "incorrigibly good," as though goodness were a thing deserving correction: *We have tried to break her of the habit of biting her nails, but she is incorrigible.*

incredulous /in kréj ə ləs/, *adj.* Unwilling to believe; doubting; skeptical. *Incredulous* is sometimes confused with a more familiar word *incredible* (unbelievable) which has a quite different meaning. When a thing is *incredible*, it is so strange or unusual that no one will believe it; when people are *incredulous*, they are unwilling to believe; that is, they have to be shown: *Accused of having told an incredible (unbelievable) story, she supplied enough proof to convince even the most incredulous (doubting) listener.* The opposite of *incredulous*, of course, is *credulous*, which means "willing to believe almost anything": *Sylvester's friends enjoy teasing him because he is so credulous.*

insatiable /in sấ shə bə-l/, *adj.* Not capable of being satisfied; greedy; not "satisfiable": *At my expense, she demonstrated an insatiable appetite for ice cream.*

inanimate /in án ə mit/, *adj.* Not living; without life or consciousness; dull. *Animate* means "living" or "lively." *Inanimate* then means "not living, without life": *The inanimate objects in the room seemed to dance in the flickering firelight.*

EXERCISE Cross out the italicized words and write above them a word or phrase from this lesson which will give the same meaning as the crossed-out expression. (Add 10 points for each correct sentence.)

1. To a *person who believes things were better years ago,* your criticisms of today's government will be *seemingly true and reasonable.*

2. The lack of expression on the face of a *calm and sluggish* person may make you think the person is also *sad and mournful.*

3. Naturally *unwilling to believe without proof* and possessing an *"unsatisfiable"* curiosity, she has the makings of a true scientist.

4. His *freedom from punishment* amazes police who know him to be *"uncorrectable."*

5. From a distance the floating object appeared to be *without life.*

6. Her *show-off* behavior comes from an *unsatisfiable* desire to be noticed.

7. You cannot cheat on an examination *without being punished;* *"uncorrectable"* cheaters always lose out.

8. People who are *sluggish in temperament* are slow to anger, but high-strung people will become angry even at *lifeless* objects like a door.

9. Mr. Cobb is really a very pleasant person, but his *mournful* manner and his *backward-looking* views give the opposite impression.

10. Your *extremely showy* sales act will not convince anyone as *unwilling to believe what you say* as Mrs. Langella.

REVIEW EXERCISE In the blank at the right of each line, write a synonym or brief definition of the italicized word. Look back only when you find you cannot remember the meaning. (Add 5 points for each correct answer.)

1. a *beneficent* relative ....

2. *cursory* study ....

3. an *irrelevant* statement ....

4. a *candid* discussion ....

5. a dangerous *charlatan* ....

6. *coerced* by parents ....

7. *incoherent* speech ....

8. a *chronic* condition ....

9. *dubious* success ....

10. *altruistic* motives ....

11. a person who is *gregarious* ....

12. *augmented* supply   . . . .
13. always *incredulous*   . . . .
14. a *lugubrious* remark   . . . .
15. an *affable* manner   . . . .
16. a *phlegmatic* personality   . . . .
17. an *opulent* way of life   . . . .
18. a *diffident* reaction   . . . .
19. a *dogmatic* decision   . . . .
20. a *plausible* explanation   . . . .

Spelling: Foreign Phrases

As it has adopted foreign words, so English has taken certain phrases or expressions from other languages. Usually these phrases have a not quite translatable meaning or flavor, and so their original pronunciations and spellings are retained. Of course, foreign spellings can cause problems.

The following foreign phrases are some of those most commonly used in the speech and writing of English-speaking people. Pronunciation and language are given after each phrase. You must simply memorize the meaning and spelling of each phrase, including any accent marks.

ad infinitum /ad ín fə nǐ təm/ *Latin.* Without limit.

bête noire /bet nwáhr/ *French.* Anything that is an object of hate or dread; a bugaboo.

bon mot /bon mố/ *French.* A terse, witty saying.

cause célèbre /kōz sā léb r/ *French.* Any well-known controversial issue; a legal case that excites great interest.

esprit de corps /es prḗ də kor/ *French.* A spirit of enthusiasm, devotion, and support of a group to which one belongs.

faux pas /fō páh/ *French.* A false step; an offense against social convention.

ipso facto /ip sō fák tō/ *Latin.* By that very fact.

joie de vivre /zhwa də vḗv r/ *French.* Joy of living.

noblesse oblige /nō blés ō blḗzh/ *French.* Nobility obligates; used to mean that high birth or position obligates generous, noble, and honorable behavior.

non sequitur /non sék wə tər/ *Latin.* A conclusion that does not logically follow from the premises.

pièce de résistance /pyes də rā zē stáns/ *French.* The principal or most important work in a series or a collection.

pro tempore /prō tém pə rē/ *Latin.* For the time being; temporarily.

raison d' être /re zón dé tr/ *French.* Reason or excuse for existing.

savoir faire /sa vwahr fǎr/ *French.* Knowing how to do and say the right thing; tact.

sotto voce /sót ō vó chē/ *Italian.* Softly, in an undertone; privately.

EXERCISE A Choose ten of the fifteen foreign phrases taught in this lesson and use each in a separate sentence that shows understanding of the phrase. (Add 10 points for each correctly used word.)

1. . . . .
2. . . . .
3. . . . .
4. . . . .
5. . . . .
6. . . . .
7. . . . .
8. . . . .
9. . . . .
10. . . . .

EXERCISE B Be ready to write from dictation the fifteen phrases taught in this lesson.

EXERCISE C With someone to record them on the board, make a class list of ten other foreign phrases. Pronounce the phrases correctly and be sure you know the meaning of each. Copy the ten phrases into your notebook. Look at each phrase. Say it correctly. Memorize the spelling, along with any accent marks. When the phrases have been erased from the board, be prepared to write them from dictation. (Add 10 points for each correctly spelled phrase.)

1. . . . .   6. . . . .
2. . . . .   7. . . . .
3. . . . .   8. . . . .
4. . . . .   9. . . . .
5. . . . .   10. . . . .

REVIEW EXERCISE   Complete each French loan word below by writing *eau, é, t, s, gue,* or *eur* in the blank. The meaning of the word is given in parentheses. (Add 10 points for each correctly spelled word.)

1. va........(unclear)

2. chauff........(a driver)

3. debri........(rubble)

4. pass........(out of style)

5. chap........(a hat)

6. consomm........(a clear soup)

7. debu........(a first appearance)

8. chale........(a Swiss cottage)

9. saut........(to fry gently)

10. fati........(weariness)

Part Two
IMPROVING SENTENCES

CHAPTER FIVE

Sentence Completeness

When a sentence fragment appears in the work of a professional writer, you can be sure that the writer wrote the fragment deliberately. Sentence fragments in the work of a high school student, however, are almost always considered evidence of incompetence. The fault may simply be due to carelessness, but the reader concludes that the writer simply does not know what a sentence is. Since sentence fragments suggest incompetence, all your writing should be done in complete sentences, with the exception, of course, of dialogue. Although we all speak fragments, we should not write them.

LESSON 33

Correcting Sentence Fragments

A sentence fragment is a part of a sentence which has been left standing by itself as though it were a sentence. Since most fragments in student writing are the result of carelessness, students usually find it easy to correct fragments which are called to their attention.

You should be able to recognize and correct four common kinds of fragments. Each of the following constructions must be written as part of a sentence. It must not be permitted to stand alone.

1. The Prepositional Phrase Fragment

FRAGMENT   I didn't have nerve enough to ask any questions. *After the teacher's long and careful explanation.*

CORRECTED   I didn't have nerve enough to ask any questions after the teacher's long and careful explanation.

2. The Verbal Phrase Fragment

A. *Participial Phrase Fragment*

FRAGMENT   Somebody had ransacked the storeroom. *Leaving boxes, barrels, and cans strewn about.*

CORRECTED   Somebody had ransacked the storeroom, <u>leaving boxes, barrels, and cans strewn about.</u>

B. *Gerund Phrase Fragment*

FRAGMENT   We started out late at night on the drive across the desert. *But not before checking gas, oil, water, and tires.*

CORRECTED   We started out late at night on the drive across the desert, <u>but not before checking gas, oil, water, and tires.</u>

C. *Infinitive Phrase Fragment*

FRAGMENT   All our friends gathered around. *To persuade us to wait till morning.*

CORRECTED   All our friends gathered around <u>to persuade us to wait till morning.</u>

3. The Appositive Fragment

FRAGMENT   Everyone went sleigh riding on Christmas. *A clear, cold day with brilliant sunshine.*

CORRECTED   Everyone went sleigh riding on Christmas, <u>a clear, cold day with brilliant sunshine.</u>

4. The Subordinate Clause Fragment

FRAGMENT   Our bus finally rolled into view. *Just as we had almost given up hope.*

CORRECTED   Our bus finally rolled into view, <u>just as we had almost given up hope.</u>

FRAGMENT   Your application should be signed by your principal. *Who knows you well enough to vouch for you.*

CORRECTED   Your application should be signed by your principal, <u>who knows you well enough to vouch for you.</u>

EXERCISE   Fragments occur almost always because a writer cuts off from a sentence a final idea that belongs in the sentence. In this exercise you will find many examples of this error. Some of the following contain fragments; others contain sentences only. Mark with an *F* those which contain a fragment. Mark with an *S* those which contain only sentences. Then remove the period and capital letter which separate the fragment from the sentence to which it belongs. A comma may be required in place of the period, but you will not be marked off for incorrect commas. (Add 5 points for each correctly marked item.)

F. A. You should stand several feet away, *i*f you wish to get the full effect of the picture.

S. B. Georgia O'Keeffe is a painter. Her work is now quite valuable.

.... 1. A young person without education is like a car without fuel. Not going anywhere.

.... 2. Today a large number of people go to college. Simply because times have changed and a college education is essential for many jobs.

.... 3. First make up your mind as to what you would like to be doing twenty years hence. Then find out what education you must have to achieve this goal.

.... 4. All nations and all councils of the United Nations must work together harmoniously. Since each group depends upon the other groups.

.... 5. Since 1946 the United Nations has been trying to eliminate atomic weapons. At the same time seeking reduction of other armaments.

.... 6. Many television programs present to the immature mind a vivid picture of crime and violence. Although the moral is usually that crime and violence cannot be committed with impunity, some people think more about the excitement of evildoing than about the moral.

.... 7. Two things I learned from my parents. The ability to distinguish right from wrong and a desire to do right.

.... 8. I plan to join the navy because the navy will prepare me for a career as an electrician. And because I like ships and travel.

.... 9. In Arabian history the compass is referred to as "southpointing." The Persian and Turkish names for the compass mean "south-pointer." Although the European mariners' compass has always pointed north, all compasses used by surveyors and astronomers pointed south as late as 1670.

.... 10. I think that slowly but surely peace will come to the world. Maybe not in our time but eventually.

.... 11. Most lightning flashes do not pass between the clouds and the earth. They go from cloud to cloud or around the edge of one cloud. The effect is clearly discernible from above as John Glenn reported after orbiting the earth.

.... 12. When you are a senior, you begin to realize what mistakes you have made in high school. What courses you should have taken. And what activities you might have joined.

.... 13. Sally's perpetually serious manner gives a fallacious impression of her personality. Which is really cheerful and affable.

.... 14. Although Senator Wong's views are reactionary, they are by no means obsolete. Her critics underestimate the popularity of her opinions. She has a large, loyal, and vocal following.

.... 15. Susan's success as an actress is almost incredible. Especially to those of us who knew her as a child. She was the most diffident and the least gregarious child I have ever known.

.... 16. The best mystery novels are packed with exciting details. That seem unconnected and confusing at first. But finally fit together into a neat and plausible pattern.

.... 17. Avid readers of mysteries usually finish a whole novel in one or two sittings. Because they are so eager to find out who "done" it?

.... 18. The most popular of mystery novelists usually create a memorable detective. Who appears in a series of books and has a loyal following of readers.

.... 19. Each fictional detective has an individual style of sleuthing. For instance, Lord Peter Wimsey, the aristocratic detective created by Dorothy Sayers, an English theologian, in the 1920's.

.... 20. Arthur Conan Doyle, Agatha Christie, Erle Stanley Gardener, and Dashiell Hammett are other authors who created ingenious characters. Although Hammett's creation, Sam Spade, appeared in only one novel, *The Maltese Falcon*.

Avoiding the Run-on Sentence

Avoid the run-on sentence. Do not use a comma between sentences. Do not omit punctuation at the end of a sentence.

When a comma is used between sentences without a coordinating conjunction (*and, but, or, for*), the result is a *run-on* sentence. Since the comma is not an end mark, it permits one sentence to run on into the next sentence.

RUN-ON   For two days winds of gale force drove the steady rain against our tent, our clothing, food, and bedding became soggy.

CORRECTED   For two days winds of gale force drove the steady rain against our tent. Our clothing, food, and bedding became soggy.

A less common kind of run-on sentence results from the omission of punctuation between sentences.

RUN-ON   We will take the 4:19 from New York it is the fastest train.

CORRECTED   We will take the 4:19 from New York. It is the fastest train.

As shown by the preceding examples, a run-on sentence may be easily corrected by inserting correct punctuation between the sentences. Often a better method of correction is the revision of the sentences.

RUN-ON   Harriet did not try out for the basketball team, she needed more time for her studies.

CORRECTED   Harriet did not try out for the basketball team **because** she needed more time for her studies.

EXERCISE A   The following paragraphs are written without end marks. Commas have been used between sentences to show the effect of the run-on sentence. Change to end marks all commas that come between sentences, and add capital letters as required. Be sure not to leave any run-on sentences or sentence fragments. (Add 10 points for each correctly marked sentence.)

1   Light sailplanes can take advantage of the slightest updrafts caused
2   by upward movements of warm air called thermals, these radiate upward
3   wherever the sun warms a patch of ground more rapidly than the area
4   around it, sailplanes must be towed aloft by powered planes and re-
5   leased, then the pilots try to gain more altitude by hopping from updraft
6   to updraft, they can gain thousands of feet in this way.
7   Soaring is the art of staying aloft and in progress on hot air, flights
8   of more than 500 miles have been recorded, and endurance records of
9   more than twenty hours, gliding bears the same relationship to powered

82

10 flight as sailing bears to power boating, that's why glider pilots look
11 contemptuously at powered planes, at least for the purposes of sport.
12   Instead of the roar and vibration of the motor, sailplane pilots have
13 silence, even at an altitude of 400 feet they can hear voices on the
14 ground, a train whistle from as high as a mile, except for the occasional
15 whisper of the wind, the pilots enjoy a world of silence and beauty,
16 fleecy clouds and bright sky and the brown and green earth far below
17 contribute their special effects.

EXERCISE B By inserting correct punctuation and capital letters, combine the word groups in the following paragraphs into complete and correctly punctuated sentences. (Add 10 points for each correct answer.)

1   In recent years many programs for the international exchange of
2 students have been developed programs which recognize that living in
3 a foreign country, close to its people, is the best way to learn about
4 another culture
5   a distinctive feature of this development has been the number of
6 students of high school age who have crossed the Atlantic European
7 and African young people have come to the United States and American
8 young people have gone to Europe and Africa the students live in
9 average homes and attend the public schools some stay for two months
10 others remain as long as a year time and funds are usually provided
11 for travel in the country under the care of competent guides who help
12 the visitors to see what they want to see

Chapter Review

In the following paragraphs, by any means you wish, remove the fragments and correct the run-on sentences. (Add 10 points for each correct answer in sentence division.)

1   The kinds of fishing constitute entirely different sports. When some
2 people say they are going fishing, they may be going to take a long
3 rest. Or heading for one of the most strenuous of sports. Indolent anglers,

4   resting their backs against tree trunks, hats tilted over their eyes, bamboo
5   poles precariously propped over the bank of a quiet stream, are hardly
6   fishing at all. They are resting. On the other hand, the insatiable trout
7   anglers stand in water for hours, braced against the rushing current of
8   a cold mountain stream. Casting again and again into the quiet pools
9   along the banks. They seek the thrill of the powerful strike, the quick,
10 flashing struggle to net their catch, they get little rest. They may return
11 home mentally refreshed. But physically tired.

12   Holding a line over the gunwale of a drifting rowboat on a June
13 evening is a tranquil occupation. Enjoyed more for the quiet and beauty
14 of the outdoors than for the catch. If, indeed, there should be any catch
15 at all. The phlegmatic rowboat anglers abstain from vigorous exercise
16 but return relaxed and ready for a good night's sleep. Unconcerned that
17 there won't be fish for breakfast. Yet we say they have been fishing just
18 as we say it of the more affluent anglers who spend the day in their
19 cabin cruisers in deep water. Fighting with marlin, tuna, or shark. These
20 anglers like nothing so much as the long, exhausting struggle, their arms
21 and backs weak with the strain of playing their catch. They enjoy the
22 suspense, their catch may break away, a larger fish may take it from
23 them. But see their proud smiles as they stand beside their hundred-
24 pounders to have their pictures taken for the folks back home.

LESSON 36

Cumulative Review

Insert capital letters and punctuation in the following passage. Remove sentence
fragments and run-on sentences. (Add 4 points for each correctly marked line.)

1   In a dispatch published in the New York Times and copyrighted by
2   the North American newspaper alliance Victor Von Hagen tells of his
3   expedition to Peru. Associated with the American Geographic society
4   the expedition set out to study the 2000-mile highway. Built by the Incas
5   500 years ago. For a long time archaeologists have doubted the veracity

84

© 1977 HBJ

6   of early spanish writers concerning the courier system of the Incas,

7   however Mr. Von Hagens investigations have supported their claims and

8   the world may now accept them as true.

9   According to the Spaniards stories the Incas had a system of relay

10   stations. Approximately two miles apart along the great Inca roads from

11   Chile to Colombia. And from the Pacific ocean to the Amazon valley.

12   The mail carriers who were called *chasquis* were stationed at the relay

13   stations, they were runners lent by neighboring tribes.

14   Each station was built high enough above the surrounding ground

15   to enable a waiting runner there to see the other runner coming, as

16   the runners met briefly a message was transferred from one to the other

17   and the fresh carrier dashed away to the next station. Since no runner

18   had to travel more than two or three miles a high speed could be

19   maintained. By this simple efficient method news traveled with speed.

20   The Americans found in the Andes mountains a part of the old road.

21   With six of these stations within a distance of fifteen miles. It did not

22   seem plausible that *chasquis* running night and day through this difficult

23   country could cover fourteen hundred miles in five days. Mr. Von Hagen

24   decided to find out, he tried it with American Indian runners. Who

25   found that they were able to equal the Incas performance.

LESSON 37

Building Vocabulary

audacious /au dắ shəs/, *adj.* Daring, bold, adventurous. *Audacious* is commonly used to mean *too bold* or *too daring: Teresa's audacious spirit sometimes gets her into trouble.*—audacity /au dás ə tē/, *n. Her audacity in accusing the mayor of dishonesty aroused the admiration of the public.*

enigma /i níg mə/, *n.* A riddle; a puzzling problem or statement: *To other members of the Security Council, the Russian delegates were always an enigma.*—enigmatic /én ig mát ik/, *adj. Had she not spoken in such enigmatic terms, we might have understood her better.*

facetious /fə sḗ shəs/, *adj.* Humorous, funny; trying to be humorous: *We were annoyed by his facetious reply to our serious question.*

immaculate /i mák yə lit/, *adj.* Spotlessly clean, pure (*im*[not] + *maculate*[spotted]): *Captain Binne keeps an immaculate ship.*—immaculately, *adv. Joan is always immaculately dressed.*

implacable /im plắ kə bə-l/, *adj.* Impossible to pacify, calm, or appease: *Implacable in his desire for conquest, the dictator refused to listen to the advice of his counselors. Her implacable attitude destroyed our hope of gaining a compromise.*

85

inexplicable /in éks pli kə bə-l/, *adj.* Unexplainable: *Her teachers were puzzled by her inexplicable behavior.*

irrevocable /ir rév ə kə bə-l/, *adj.* Impossible to withdraw, cancel, revoke (call back) (*ir*[not] + *revocable*["recallable"]): *Once it has been made, my decision will be irrevocable.*

latent /lā́ tənt/, *adj.* In existence but hidden or concealed: *The latent power of the atom is immense. He revealed a hitherto latent desire to control others.*

pernicious /pər nísh əs/, *adj.* Causing harm; very injurious, wicked: *Always a troublemaker, she is a pernicious influence on her classmates.*

propriety /prə prī́ ə tē/, *n.* Fitness, suitability, proper behavior: *I question the propriety of your overruling the principal.* Antonym: *impropriety. The audience was shocked by the impropriety of the speaker's criticism of the treasurer.*

EXERCISE Write before each word the letter of the best meaning from the list at the right. (Add 5 points for each correct answer.)

.... 1. immaculate

.... 2. enigma

.... 3. facetious

.... 4. implacable

.... 5. propriety

.... 6. latent

.... 7. audacious

.... 8. inexplicable

.... 9. pernicious

.... 10. irrevocable

a. humorous

b. bold

c. puzzle

d. unexplainable

e. spotless

f. injurious

g. hidden

h. impossible to cancel

i. impossible to appease

j. proper behavior

Each number and blank represents one of the ten words in this lesson. Write the appropriate word in each blank.

a. With one (11).................... move, the team seized the initiative, and their hitherto (12).................... power began to show itself.

b. I doubt the (13).................... of your lightheartedly taking a (14).................... attitude toward such a grave matter.

c. In her desire for revenge, she was (15)....................; once made, her decisions were (16)....................

d. One way to reduce the danger of (17).................... germs is to keep the hospital in a(n) (18).................... condition.

e. To the police the case remains a(n) (19)....................; it is apparently one of those (20).................... crimes.

REVIEW EXERCISE This exercise presents a number of problems involving the relationship in meaning between paired words. The problems are stated as a proportion is stated in mathematics.

A. day:(is to) night::(as) tall:(is to)..............

Having noted that the relationship between the first two words is that of opposites, you will complete the statement so that the second pair of words will also be opposites; the word *short* should be written in the blank. *Day*:(*is to*) *night*::(*as*) *tall*:(*is to*) *short*. As a trial run, fill in the blank in each statement below with one of the words from the column at the right. First discover the relationship between the first two words in each statement and then supply the word which will make the same relationship between the second two words. Answers are given in the footnote on page 95.

1. many:numerous::strong:................   instruct

2. spark:fire::................:fight   thoughtful

3. scholar:study::teacher:................   powerful

4. miser:selfish::philosopher:................   quarrel

5. left:right::................:cruelty   kindness

Fill the blank in each item below with one of the following words. (Add 10 points for each correct answer.)

avaricious   eccentric   immaculate   lethargic   pernicious
dogmatic   facetious   irrelevant   opulence   reactionary

1. loquacious:talkative::....................:humorous

2. audacious:diffident::pertinent:....................

3. precarious:dubious::....................:injurious

4. adamant:amenable::........................:progressive (forward-looking)

5. enigma:inexplicable::bigot:....................

6. coherent:lucidity::lucrative:....................

7. charlatan:veracious::altruist:....................

8. indolence:laziness::phlegmatic:....................

9. plebeian:aristocratic::normal:....................

10. abstinent:indulgent::....................:dirty

LESSON 38

Spelling: New Words in the Language

Our English language is a living thing and, like all living things, it is constantly changing. Among the changes that take place are those involving vocabulary. Old words die out; current words change in meaning or usage; and new words enter. Many new words, such as most slang expressions, are usually quite short-lived, but others, those that are the result of new inventions, discoveries, materials, changes in society, or explorations, enter the standard vocabulary of our language.

New words, like old ones, may sometimes pose spelling problems. Troublesome spelling spots in the new words below are printed in red.

aerospace	hydrofoil
astronaut	hydroponics
astrophysics	microfilm
automation	montage
benzedrine	motorcade
boutique	racism
collage	Sanforize
cybernetics	scofflaw
cyclotron	supersonic
discothèque	telethon
extrasensory	totalitarian
helicopter	transistor

xerography

EXERCISE A Choose ten of the words taught in this lesson, and use each in a separate sentence that shows understanding of its meaning. (Check a dictionary for the meaning of any words that are unfamiliar to you.) (Add 10 points for each properly used word.)

1. ....
2. ....
3. ....
4. ....
5. ....
6. ....
7. ....
8. ....
9. ....
10. ....

EXERCISE B Be prepared to write from dictation the twenty-five words taught in this lesson.

EXERCISE C With someone recording them on the board, make a class list of ten other new words that have caused spelling problems. Try to determine which letter or letters cause the difficulty in each word. Copy the list in your notebook. It will then be erased from the board. Study your list and be prepared to write it from dictation. (Add 10 points for each correctly spelled word.)

1. . . . .   6. . . . .

2. . . . .   7. . . . .

3. . . . .   8. . . . .

4. . . . .   9. . . . .

5. . . . .   10. . . . .

REVIEW EXERCISE Complete the foreign phrases below by writing the missing letters in the blanks. The meaning of each phrase is given in parentheses. (Add 20 points for each correctly spelled phrase.)

1. sotto vo. . . . . . .(in an undertone)

2. fau. . . . . . . pa. . . . . . .(a mistake in etiquette)

3. non seq. . . . . . .(an illogical conclusion)

4. bon m. . . . . . .(a witty remark)

5. ad infin. . . . . . .(limitless)

CHAPTER SIX

Improving Sentences Through Subordination

The sentences written by children are often a series of independent clauses joined by the coordinating conjunctions *and, but,* and *or.*

We were coming home from school, and we saw two big dogs, but we stopped, and they ran away.

This is a childish sentence because it makes every idea of equal importance and does not try to show how the ideas are related. A mature writer would express the same ideas in such a way that the sentence would show which ideas are more important and just how the ideas are related.

As she was coming home from school, she saw two big dogs, but *when* she stopped, they ran away.

This sentence contains two subordinate[1] clauses which express the less important ideas (*as she was coming home from school* and *when she stopped*); furthermore, by means of the subordinating conjunctions *as* and *when,* the writer makes clear the *time relationship* between the subordinate ideas and the main ideas.

This chapter will give you practice in writing mature sentences in which you subordinate ideas. Sentence ideas may be subordinated by being expressed in subordinate clauses, phrases, or appositives.

LESSON 39

Subordination Through Adverb Clauses

Use adverb clauses to make clear the relationship between ideas within a sentence.

An adverb clause begins with a subordinating conjunction which serves two purposes. It joins the clause to the rest of the sentence, and it shows the relationship between the idea in the subordinate clause and the idea in the rest of the sentence. For example, these two ideas are to be included in the same sentence:

1. We have been having regular fire-safety inspections.
2. Our school buildings are probably safer today than ever before.

---

[1] *Subordinate* means literally "of a lower order or rank." (*Sub-* means "under" or "below—lower"; the root *-ord-* means "order or rank.")

Before you write the sentence, ask yourself how these ideas are related. You will probably decide that the relationship is one of cause and effect. The regular inspections, in other words, have caused (or brought about) the greater safety of school buildings. This relationship can be expressed by the subordinating conjunction *because,* and we shall have a clear sentence:

Because we have been having regular fire-safety inspections, our school buildings are probably safer today than ever before.

This process of selecting the exact conjunction with which to relate a subordinate idea to a main idea is the most important aspect of using adverb clauses.

Make clear the relationship between the idea in an adverb clause and the ideas in the rest of the sentence by selecting a subordinating conjunction which expresses the relationship exactly.

TIME	after	before	until	whenever
	as	since	when	while
CAUSE OR REASON	as	because	since	whereas
PURPOSE OR RESULT	that	so that	in order that	
CONDITION	although	provided	unless	if

EXERCISE By selecting an appropriate conjunction, combine the two sentences in each of the following pairs into one clear sentence. Follow these steps: (1) Determine the relationship between the two sentences. Write this relationship in the space at the left. (2) Select from the list of subordinating conjunctions the one which you think will best express this relationship. Write it in the space provided in the sentence. Many of the blanks may be acceptably filled by various conjunctions. Change punctuation and capital letters as necessary. (Add 5 points for each correctly handled sentence.)

Relationship

...*condition*... A. .....*If*..... You get your driver's license before June, You can get a job at Kornfield's delivering orders.

.... 1. .... Some states are poorer than others. The federal government should try to help the poor states financially to provide schools equal to those in the rich states.

.... 2. .... Federal aid becomes effective. All Americans will have equal educational opportunities.

.... 3. .... You can afford to give up several hours a day to practice. You should not take expensive voice lessons.

. . . . 4. There isn't much fame or glory in intramural sports. . . . . They are played solely for the fun of the game.

. . . . 5. . . . . You may not enjoy a certain assembly program. Propriety dictates that you should sit quietly and behave courteously.

. . . . 6. The course in typing was especially valuable to me. . . . . My poor handwriting invariably prejudiced teachers against my work.

. . . . 7. . . . . You try to start the motor. Pull the choke out as far as it will go.

. . . . 8. Students should earn their own spending money. . . . . They will have a greater appreciation of the value of money.

. . . . 9. She did not change her mind. . . . . She saw that the majority were implacably against her.

. . . . 10. . . . . I grow older and more mature. My ideas about life constantly change.

. . . . 11. Taking a facetious attitude in a serious discussion gets you nowhere. . . . . People resent having their sincere beliefs treated lightly.

. . . . 12. . . . . Many influential people were against her. Anne Royall was successful.

. . . . 13. . . . . You want to decide whether something you desire to do is right or wrong. Ask yourself candidly whether you would want all your friends to know about it.

. . . . 14. I want to date many people. . . . . I will be able to meet the best person for me.

. . . . 15. . . . . I decided to get a summer job. I made a list of the places I would like to work.

. . . . 16. I can usually stay after school to attend a club meeting or work on the newspaper. . . . . My teachers have given me a lot of homework.

. . . . 17. . . . . Isadora Duncan began doing free-form, interpretive dancing. The devotees of traditional, classical dancing condemned her performances as crude and artless.

.... 18. The Air Force is continually experimenting with
                     safety equipment............ It can increase the
                     margin of safety for its pilots.

.... 19. .... Your car skids on the ice. Turn the
                     wheels in the direction of the skid.

.... 20. You will not get ahead in business............ You
                     take some risks.

Subordination Through Adjective Clauses

Use adjective clauses to make clear the relative emphasis to be given ideas in a sentence.

You have learned that the adverb clause helps you to express clearly certain relationships between sentence ideas. The adjective clause, which begins with a relative pronoun (*who, whom, whose, which, that*), gives important information about the word the clause modifies. This information is placed in a subordinate position and thus receives less stress, less emphasis, than that given in the independent clause. Note the difference in emphasis in the following sentences.

1. The small motor, <u>which is in the rear of the car</u>, develops amazing power.
2. The small motor, <u>which develops amazing power</u>, is in the rear of the car.

The two sentences are equally good sentences. They differ only in emphasis. In the first sentence the idea that the motor is in the rear of the car is placed in a subordinate clause, where it receives less emphasis than the other idea—that the motor develops amazing power. In the second sentence the emphasis is reversed. The important idea is that the motor is in the rear of the car.

EXERCISE Reverse the emphasis in each of the following sentences by placing in an adjective clause the idea now in the independent clause. In the space below each sentence, write the new clause. (Add 10 points for each correct clause.)

A. The White House, which was originally called the President's Palace, is known officially as the Executive Mansion.

... *which is known officially as the Executive Mansion* ...

1. Washington, who laid the cornerstone, never lived in the White House.

....

2. Abigail Adams, who was the first President's wife to live in the house, used to hang her washing in the uncompleted East Room.

....

3. The building, which had been altered and enlarged by many Presidents, was declared unsafe in 1948.

. . . .

4. Reconstruction, which was completed in 1952, cost over five million dollars.

. . . .

5. The White House, which is a national symbol as well as a residence, has 132 rooms and 20 baths.

. . . .

6. Blair House, which was the home of one of Lincoln's advisers, is the President's guest house.

. . . .

7. Private Presidential homes, which are now historic sites, are visited by thousands every year.

. . . .

8. Monticello, which is near Charlottesville, Virginia, was the home of Thomas Jefferson.

. . . .

9. Mt. Vernon, which is the most famous of all Presidential residences, was in the Washington family for several generations.

. . . .

10. Theodore Roosevelt's home, Sagamore Hill, which became a national historic site in 1962, is in Oyster Bay, New York.

. . . .

LESSON 41

Correcting Faulty Coordination

When a coordinating conjunction like *and* is used to join ideas that are not equal or are related in some way other than that of addition, the coordination is said to be faulty.

Faulty coordination may be corrected by placing one of the sentence ideas in a subordinate clause, either an adverb clause beginning with if, when, although, unless, etc., or an adjective clause beginning with who, whom, whose, which, or that.

© 1977 HBJ

And is the most frequently used coordinating conjunction. It expresses the idea of addition. An unskillful writer, however, may try to make *and* do work more properly done by a subordinating conjunction. If the relationship between sentence ideas is that of *time, cause, purpose, result,* or *condition, and* cannot do the job so well as a subordinating conjunction.

EXERCISE   The sentences in this exercise are examples of faulty coordination. Cross out the *and* and place one of the ideas in a subordinate clause—either an adverb clause or an adjective clause—which will express more accurately the relationship between the sentence ideas. Occasionally one or two words other than *and* will have to be crossed out. (Add 10 points for each correct sentence.)

A. *When*
A. A privately financed communications satellite was launched in 1962, ~~and~~ international television became a reality.

1. Many critics believed that George Bernard Shaw was interested mainly in expressing ideas, and they did not consider him an effective dramatist.

2. One of Shaw's most famous characters, Henry Higgins in *Pygmalion,* is an expert on British dialects, and many people think that Shaw was an Englishman.

3. George Bernard Shaw was born in Dublin in 1856, and he was undeniably an Irishman.

4. Shaw attended four schools, and he received his real education at home.

5. In 1891 Shaw had still not written a play, and he was thirty-five years old.

6. A dozen years later Shaw called himself "an unperformed playwright in London," and he had written twelve plays.

7. His plays were performed on stage, and the audiences reacted very favorably.

8. Shaw considered himself a second Shakespeare, and he knew all of Shakespeare's works thoroughly.

9. Readers will evaluate the total body of his work, and they will discover one of the most prolific writers of the twentieth century.

10. His plays and prefaces alone represent a tremendous literary output, and they are only half his total writing.

Answers to "trial run" on page 87: 1. powerful; 2. quarrel; 3. instruct; 4. thoughtful; 5. kindness.

Subordination Through Phrases and Appositives

Subordinate clauses can be used to improve sentences by clarifying the relationship between ideas and permitting emphasis of one idea over another. You can also subordinate ideas by placing them in phrases and appositives. Like subordination through clauses, subordination through phrases and appositives enables you to combine several ideas into one smooth sentence.

Subordination Through Phrases Observe how the following ideas are combined into one sentence by placing two of the ideas in phrases.

IDEAS (Rita took a firm grip on the fence top) (she made a superhuman effort) (she pulled herself over to the other side)

COMBINED Taking a firm grip on the fence top (*participial phrase*), Rita, by a superhuman effort (*prepositional phrase*), pulled herself over to the other side.

Subordination Through Appositives An appositive is a noun or pronoun—often with modifiers—that follows another noun or pronoun to identify or explain it.

EXAMPLES Myung-Wha Chung, a cellist, will be the soloist at our spring concert.
Karl audaciously enrolled in advanced calculus, an extremely difficult course.

An appositive functions like an adjective clause.

ADJECTIVE CLAUSE The European Common Market, which is a cooperative enterprise of several nations, was formed to stimulate economic growth in Europe.

APPOSITIVE The European Common Market, a cooperative enterprise of several nations, was formed to stimulate economic growth in Europe.

EXERCISE Show that you understand how to subordinate sentence ideas through phrases and appositives as you combine the ideas in each group below into one smooth sentence. Express as many of the ideas in phrases or appositives as you can. Do not write any subordinate clauses. Changes in wording and the order of ideas are permitted, provided they do not change the meaning. Suggestions are given for the first five groups. (Add 10 points for each correct sentence.)

A. (the driver ahead of me signaled for a right turn) (he nearly caused a serious crash) (he turned left) [Begin with "Signaling for a right turn . . ."]

. . Signaling for a right turn, the driver ahead of . .
. . me turned left, nearly causing a serious crash. . . .

1. (Carla grew up in Greenport) (Greenport is a busy fishing and boating center) (Carla learned a lot about boats and the sea) [Begin with "Growing up in Greenport . . ."]

....
....
....

2. (there was a recent survey of physical fitness) (it tested boys and girls in American schools) (26 per cent of the boys and 23 per cent of the girls failed the minimum test) [Begin with "In a recent survey . . ."]

....
....
....

3. (six Americans climbed the southeast spur of Mt. McKinley) (they did it in twenty-six days) (Mt. McKinley is the tallest mountain in North America) [Begin with "In twenty-six days . . ."]

....
....
....

4. (the climbers were approaching the peak) (they had to cross a great glacier) (the glacier was filled with dangerous crevasses) [Begin with "Approaching the peak . . ."]

....
....
....

5. (Rafael cleared the bar with ease) (he set a new meet record) (he is captain of the track team) [Begin with "Clearing the bar . . ."]

....
....
....

6. (Antonia won the chess match) (she planned her strategy very carefully) (she won in ten bold moves)

....
....
....

7. (the friends set out before dawn) (they were going on a fishing trip) (they hoped to start fishing at daylight)

....

....

....

8. (students are organizing a discussion) (they will discuss a longer school day) (this longer day is proposed by the Board of Education)

....

....

....

9. (snow fell all night) (it was blown by strong winds) (it formed impassable drifts)

....

....

....

10. (the freshman dance was held on Halloween) (it was a costume party) (it attracted a large crowd) (the crowd was composed mostly of seniors)

....

....

....

LESSON 43

Avoiding Stringy Sentences

Use subordinate clauses, phrases, and appositives to avoid stringy sentences.

A sentence becomes stringy when it is composed of a number of independent clauses strung together by *and, but, and so, so, or.* Stringy sentences make monotonous reading. More serious than their monotony, however, is their complete lack of subordination and the fact that they often contain examples of faulty coordination. Both of these weaknesses affect meaning. If you use subordination through clauses, phrases, and appositives, avoiding the conjunctions *and, but, and so, so, or,* your sentences will not be stringy. Notice how the stringy sentences below have been improved.

STRINGY   People build an artificial front for themselves, and they hope to impress others, but others always see through their front, and so it is useless.

98

CORRECTED   When people build an artificial front for themselves (*subordinate clause*), hoping to impress others (*participial phrase*), the front is useless (*independent clause*) because others always see through it (*subordinate clause*).

STRINGY   America has had a large reserve of foodstuff until now, and we Americans have given or sold surplus food to less developed countries, and India is such a country, and overpopulation in India is an enormous problem, and it has lead to widespread hunger.

CORRECTED   Since America has had a large reserve of foodstuff until now (*subordinate clause*), we Americans have given or sold surplus food to less developed countries (*independent clause*), like India (*prepositional phrase*), where overpopulation, which led to widespread hunger, is an enormous problem (*subordinate clauses*).

EXERCISE On the lines below each of the following stringy sentences, rewrite the sentence, eliminating the conjunctions *and, and so, so, but, or* by placing most of the ideas in subordinate constructions. Changes in wording or the order of ideas are permitted, provided they do not change the meaning. Use the following methods of subordination. (Add 10 points for each properly constructed sentence.)

Adverb clause: begins with such words as *although, when, because, if,* etc.
Adjective clause: begins with *who, whom, whose, which, that*
Adverb phrase or *adjective phrase:* begins with a preposition
Participial phrase: contains a participle
Appositive

1. The group paraded up Tenth Street, and it caused a big traffic jam, and so the police have refused permission for any more demonstrations.

   . . . .
   . . . .
   . . . .

2. I know the classics are important, but I read mostly modern novels, and I think modern literature is more interesting.

   . . . .
   . . . .
   . . . .

3. Flower Boulevard is a wide street, and it has spacious lawns, and its homes are magnificent, and it is the most beautiful street in town.

   . . . .
   . . . .
   . . . .

4. You can save money by flying off-season, but you can save even more by taking the bus, and the bus is cheaper than the plane or the train.

. . . .

. . . .

. . . .

5. Peter J. McGuire was the founder of the Carpenters' Union, and he originally suggested the idea of a Labor Day, and it was first celebrated in New York on September 3, 1882.

. . . .

. . . .

. . . .

6. The name of Charlotte Perkins Gilman is almost unknown today but her book was widely read in the first two decades of the twentieth century, and *Women and Economics* was concerned with achieving full equality for women in an industrial society.

. . . .

. . . .

. . . .

7. A questionnaire was sent to class presidents in high schools in New York State, and the students were asked to name their favorite writer, and Emily Brontë was the first choice.

. . . .

. . . .

. . . .

8. California today ranks third in gold production, and it was the scene of the first great Gold Rush, and this was started by James Marshall at Sutter's sawmill, and it was started in 1848.

. . . .

. . . .

. . . .

9. Diplomats are constantly confronting the enigmas of international politics, and they must always be ready to negotiate, and the alternative to talk is likely to be war.

. . . .

. . . .

10. By themselves Presidents could never gain detailed knowledge of all the departments of government, and so they must rely on their advisers, and they are members of the White House staff, or they are members of the Cabinet.

. . . .

. . . .

. . . .

. . . .

Chapter Review

Using the various means of subordination which you have studied in this chapter, combine the ideas in each group below into one clear, smooth sentence. (Add 10 points for each properly constructed sentence.)

1. (Lillian decided to become a doctor) (she was sixteen) (she was working in Dr. De Soto's office)

. . . .

. . . .

. . . .

2. (you can see that clear penmanship is worth money) (half a million income-tax refund checks go undelivered annually) (the taxpayer's signature or address is illegible)

. . . .

. . . .

. . . .

. . . .

3. (in summer the school libraries are closed) (the public library is very busy) (high school students are getting their required summer reading done)

. . . .

. . . .

. . . .

4. (for years lamprey eels had preyed on the whitefish in the Great Lakes) (they had nearly wiped out the fish) (scientists developed a chemical) (this may solve the problem by destroying eel larvae)

. . . .

. . . .

. . . .

. . . .

5. (traffic experts recommended an eight-lane highway) (the politicians wanted to save money) (they approved only a four-lane highway) (this highway is now totally inadequate)

. . . .

. . . .

. . . .

. . . .

6. (some nations disapprove of certain resolutions of the United Nations) (they refuse to abide by them) (this practice could wreck the international organization)

. . . .

. . . .

. . . .

7. (Dorothy Day was the founder of *The Catholic Worker*) (the weekly newspaper was started during the Depression) (it exposed the poverty and the exploitation of working people)

. . . .

. . . .

. . . .

8. (motor hotels in cities may be different from motels in the country) (they are not different from regular city hotels) (they provide the same luxurious accommodations for travelers)

. . . .

. . . .

. . . .

. . . .

9. (the location of the new airport was a subject of heated argument) (the problem was finally solved) (the decision was to locate it on the site of the old one) (this site was to be greatly expanded)

. . . .

. . . .

. . . .

. . . .

10. (Myra graduated from college) (then she got a job as an editorial assistant) (the job required a degree and secretarial skills) (Myra was interested in publishing)

. . . .

. . . .

. . . .

. . . .

In each of the sentences below three parts are underlined and lettered A, B, or C. Decide which of the three underlined parts is an error in capitalization, punctuation, or spelling. Write its letter in the space at the right. (Add 10 points for each correct answer.)

A. Our city does <u>it's</u> best to provide recreation for <u>children,</u>   A. .*a*.
          A   B

   <u>teen-agers,</u> and adults.
       C

1. A trip to <u>Yellowstone national park</u> in the <u>northwest</u> corner   1. .....
                 A   B

   of Wyoming is a must for everyone <u>who</u> loves natural wonders.
                                C

2. "Don't you <u>agree,"</u> asked Ms. Lawrence <u>cheerfully, "that</u> we   2. .....
            A   B

   should have a test on <u>Monday"?</u>
                   C

3. The American standard of <u>living,</u> which is the highest in the   3. .....
                       A

   <u>world,</u> will, I think, eventually be equaled by that of other
     B

   <u>country's.</u>
      ·C

4. "It's <u>better</u> <u>then</u> I <u>expected!"</u> Peter exclaimed after his first   4. .....
    A   B   C

   ride on a roller coaster.

5. The school has <u>its</u> <u>faults,</u> but the students are <u>to</u> loyal to admit   5. .....
            A   B   C

   them.

6. Sky <u>diving,</u> which is done by parachute jumpers before opening   6. .....
        A

   <u>their</u> chutes, is a dangerous <u>sport. Which</u> has attracted an
     B   C

   inexplicably large following.

7. At Lincoln High students have the same guidance <u>counselors</u>   7. .....
                                   A

   for three <u>years,</u> this system insures <u>their</u> getting adequate
            B   C

   guidance.

104

8. If you're qualified, you can take college courses in high   8. . . . . .
   ___
    A

   school, for example, my sister took Chemistry II and calculus.
   ____   _____
     B   C

9. It's generally agreed among driver education teachers that your   9. . . . . .
   ___
    A

   parents are the worst ones to give you driving instruction. Not
                                                    _____
                                                        B

   because they don't know how to drive, but because you won't
                                                            ____
                                                             C

   listen to them.

10. I hope to receive the papers in tomorrows mail; any delay will 10. . . . . .
              _____   _____   _
                 A   B   C

   be unfortunate.

Building Vocabulary

ambiguous /am bíg y-ū əs/, *adj.* Having two meanings; unclear. This word is most commonly used to describe a statement that can be understood to mean two different things. The following sentence is *ambiguous: Mary told Janet her sister would call for her.* Whose sister—Mary's or Janet's? The sentence may be interpreted in two ways. (*Ambiguous* is also used in a broader sense to describe something which is considered doubtful or uncertain: *Finding myself in an ambiguous situation, I decided to wait for someone else to make the first move.*)—am-biguity /ám bə gy-ú ə tē/, *n.* The ambiguity of the teacher's remark left us confused.

assiduous /ə síj ū əs/, *adj.* Hardworking, persistent, steadily working: *If Alice were as assiduous in her studies as she is at golf, she would be an A student.*

deprecate /dép rə kāt/, *v.* To express disapproval of someone or something: *The general publicly deprecated the actions of his lieutenant, but secretly he approved them.* (Do not confuse *deprecate* with *depreciate*, which means to lower the value of something: *The value of money is depreciated by inflation.*)

facile /fás ə-l/, *adj.* Easily done; working in an easy manner: *His facile hands completed the carving in a few hours.*—**facility** /fə síl ə tē/, *n.* Capability: *The aptitude test confirmed my facility for learning languages.*

homogeneous /hố mə jế nē əs/, *adj.* All of the same kind; composed of persons or things that are alike: *In some schools students are grouped in homogeneous classes.* Antonym: *heterogeneous. The club, composed of people of every social class, was too heterogeneous to function smoothly without constant argument.*

immutable /i my-ű tə bə-l/, *adj.* Not changeable; never changing; (*im*-[not] + *mutable* [changeable]): *The immutable position of the American delegates was well known.*

impervious /im púr vē əs/, *adj.* Impossible to penetrate or affect: *This furniture is made of a plastic which is guaranteed to be impervious to the weather. Mary, who is stubborn, was impervious to our pleading.*

obsequious /əb sế kwē əs/, *adj.* Overly polite and obedient; slavelike; fawning. *Obsequious* is most commonly used to describe persons who "bow and scrape" before someone whose favor they wish to obtain: *After his bragging, Nick surprised us by his obsequious manner in the presence of the principal.*

pecuniary /pi ky-ű nē ér ē/, *adj.* Relating to money; consisting of money; financial: *The pecuniary reward was small; the spiritual benefits were great.*

reiterate /rē ɪt ə rāt/, *v.* To repeat: *Although the warning was reiterated, the children ignored it.*

Draw a line through each italicized word or word group in the following sentences and write above it a word from this lesson which will give the same meaning as the expression you crossed out. (Add 5 points for each correct answer.)

1. The teacher *spoke disapprovingly of* the laboratory manual because of the *double-meaning* character of its directions to the students.

2. As they follow their *unchanging* course around the sun, the planets form a group *whose members are closely similar.* (Put the word before *group.*)

3. Although we sent out our most *hard-working and persistent* sales representatives, our campaign was not a *financial* success.

4. Ms. Foster *declared again* her dislike of the *bowing, slavelike, fawning* kind of employee.

5. Since all families in the town are in similar circumstances, the community has a *likeness of membership* character which outsiders are inclined to *express disapproval of.*

6. People who work only for the *financial* results of their efforts are not likely to be very *steady, hard-working* employees.

7. Although she *gave again* her opinion of our proposal, she spoke in such *double-meaning* terms that we were confused.

8. Her mind, *working in an easy manner* and *unaffected by* distractions, solved the problem in a few minutes.

9. Although outwardly *servile and obedient to authority,* he bore inwardly an *unchanging and unchangeable* contempt for his superiors.

10. Being a *smooth-working* thief, he opened the safe and, *unaffected by* the danger of being caught, calmly dropped the contents into a bag.

REVIEW EXERCISE In the space at the right, place the letter of the word which is *opposite in meaning* to the word in italics. (Add 5 points for each correct answer.)

1. *implacable* person
   a. assiduous
   b. likely to give in
   c. hard to please
   d. gregarious   1. ....

2. an act which is *irrevocable*
   a. deprecated
   b. not reversible
   c. withdrawable
   d. well-known   2. ....

3. a *latent* strength
   a. secret   b. great   c. obvious   d. valuable   3. ....

4. done *with propriety*
   a. inappropriately
   b. in a suitable manner
   c. like a proprietor
   d. convincingly
   4. . . . .

5. a *feasible* plan
   a. precarious   b. expedient   c. sound   d. impracticable   5. . . . .

6. *inexplicable* reaction
   a. easily explained
   b. phlegmatic
   c. highly emotional
   d. unaccountable
   6. . . . .

7. *immaculate* house
   a. unfinished
   b. uninhabited
   c. dirty
   d. fine
   7. . . . .

8. *facetious* attitude
   a. eccentric   b. solemn   c. amusing   d. derogatory   8. . . . .

9. *audacious* crook
   a. dangerous   b. facile   c. diffident   d. candid   9. . . . .

10. an *enigmatic* comment
    a. bewildering
    b. irrelevant
    c. pertinent
    d. clear
    10. . . . .

11. a *pernicious* law
    a. weak
    b. dangerous
    c. much-needed
    d. harmless
    11. . . . .

12. an *incredulous* audience
    a. unbelieving
    b. unbelievable
    c. easily convinced
    d. restless, uneasy
    12. . . . .

13. cheat *with impunity*
    a. with bad consequences
    b. skillfully
    c. harmlessly
    d. with good reason
    13. . . . .

14. an *insatiable* conqueror
    a. unhappy
    b. highly successful
    c. easily satisfied
    d. unsatisfactory
    14. . . . .

15. a *lugubrious* remark
    a. critical
    b. cheerful
    c. mumbled
    d. pessimistic
    15. . . . .

16. a *plausible* excuse
    a. unlikely
    b. lucrative
    c. uncertain
    d. expected
    16. . . . .

17. *incorrigible* delinquent
    a. unchangeable
    b. indolent
    c. amenable
    d. improvable
    17. . . . .

18. an *obsolete* theory
    a. questionable
    b. newly accepted
    c. absurd
    d. old-fashioned
    18. . . . .

19. *indigent* refugees
    a. opulent
    b. unwelcome
    c. welcome
    d. needy
    19. . . . .

20. an *altruist*
    a. selfish person
    b. friend
    c. insane person
    d. choice
    20. . . . .

LESSON 46

Spelling: Troublesome Scientific Words

Do not dismiss from your mind the spelling of words you learn in your science classes. You must know how to spell correctly these words from biology, chemistry, and physics. They are part of the vocabulary you need to master for the tests and papers you will be writing.

The scientific words (and their meanings) listed below often cause spelling problems. Trouble spots are printed in red.

acoustics — The science of sound; its production, transmission, and effects.

ampere — The unit of intensity of electric current produced by one volt acting through a resistance of one ohm.

catalyst — A substance that controls the rate of a chemical reaction, without changing itself.

chronometer — An extremely accurate clock or watch.

corpuscle — A protoplasmic cell, especially one of those that float free in the blood.

cyclone — A storm or system of winds, often violent, with abundant precipitation.

ductile — The ability of some types of matter to be drawn into a wire.

fission — The splitting or disintegration of a nucleus into two or more parts.

ionosphere — The highest layer of atmosphere (about fifty miles above the earth) which consists of electrons and ions.

molecule — A unit of matter; the smallest portion of an element or compound that retains chemical identity with the substance in a mass.

nucleus — The dense portion of a living cell that acts as a control center; the central part of an atom containing neutrons and protons.

osmosis — The diffusion which proceeds through a semipermeable membrane separating two solutions, and which tends to equalize their concentrations.

protoplasm — The essential substance of the cell body and nucleus of the cells of animals and plants.

seismograph — An instrument for recording shock waves and motions in the earth's crust.

stratosphere   An upper layer of the atmosphere (from ten to thirty miles up) in which the temperature changes are almost nonexistent and clouds of water never form.

EXERCISE A   Be prepared to write from dictation the words taught in this lesson.

EXERCISE B   Choose ten words from those taught and use each in a separate sentence that shows understanding of its meaning. (Add 10 points for each properly used word.)

1. ....
2. ....
3. ....
4. ....
5. ....
6. ....
7. ....
8. ....
9. ....
10. ....

EXERCISE C   With someone to record them on the board, make a class list of ten other troublesome scientific words. Copy the words in your notebook. Study in particular the letters that cause spelling problems. After the list has been erased from the board, be prepared to write the words from dictation. (Add 10 points for each correctly spelled word.)

1.	6. ....
2.	7. ....
3.	8. ....
4.	9. ....
5.	10. ....

REVIEW EXERCISE   Write the following words from dictation. (Add 10 points for each correctly spelled word.)

1. astronaut	6. helicopter
2. telethon	7. racism
3. cybernetics	8. boutique
4. collage	9. aerospace
5. xerography	10. montage

Twenty Words *Pretest—study—retest.* (Add 5 points for each correctly spelled word.)

1. ac quaint ance
2. as so ci a tion
3. bul le tin
4. cam paign
5. can di date
6. com mis sion
7. def i nite ly
8. el i gi ble
9. ex ist ence
10. guar an tee
11. in flu ence
12. med i cine
13. mu nic i pal
14. par al lel
15. prej u dice
16. pro pel ler
17. re al ize
18. rhythm
19. sim i lar
20. vil lain

CHAPTER SEVEN

Arranging Ideas Clearly in Sentences

In speaking, you vary the tone and loudness of your voice, use pauses and gestures. These actions help to make meaning clear. In writing, however, you must rely on the words alone and whatever help punctuation provides. The following sentence, for example, may be spoken with complete clarity: "Mrs. Stubbs called on her representative all dressed up in a new fur coat." When you read the sentence, you sense that something is wrong. It seems to say that the representative was wearing a new fur coat. You must read the sentence a second time to make sure what it means, which is that Mrs. Stubbs was wearing a new fur coat when she called on her representative. For the meaning to be clear, the participial phrase must be moved to a different position:

All dressed up in a new fur coat, Mrs. Stubbs called on her representative.

This chapter calls to your attention a few of the common faults in sentence structure, faults which may not be noticeable in spoken sentences but which are serious in writing. Once you have learned to recognize them, you can easily remove them from your own writing.

LESSON 47

Placing Phrase and Clause Modifiers

Place phrase and clause modifiers as near as possible to the words they modify.

A modifier makes the meaning of a word more definite. If its position in the sentence leaves any doubt as to what word it modifies, the meaning of the sentence is not clear. To assure clarity, place a modifier near the word it modifies.

NOT CLEAR   The Fire Squad staged a fire drill while classes were passing *without warning.* (The phrase *without warning* modifies *staged.* It should be placed nearer to the word it modifies.)

CLEAR   The Fire Squad **without warning** staged a fire drill while classes were passing.

ALSO CLEAR   **Without warning** the Fire Squad staged a fire drill while classes were passing.

NOT CLEAR   For the fashion show students acted as models *who had designed and made their own outfits.* (The adjective clause *who had designed and made their own outfits* modifies *students*. It should be placed nearer to the word it modifies.)

CLEAR   For the fashion show <u>students who had designed and made their own outfits</u> acted as models.

Frequently you will find it easier to improve a modifier's position if you rearrange the entire sentence.

NOT CLEAR   We enjoyed a ride in Ms. Martin's luxurious new cabin cruiser, *which lasted almost four hours.*

CLEAR   In Ms. Martin's luxurious new cabin cruiser, we enjoyed a <u>ride which lasted almost four hours</u>.

EXERCISE   Each of the following sentences contains a misplaced phrase or clause modifier. Underline this misplaced modifier and indicate by inserting a caret (∧) where the modifier should appear in the sentence. (Add 10 points for each correctly marked sentence.)

A. Passengers and crew conducted themselves ∧ as the plane descended <u>with calm efficiency</u>.

1. The story is about a man who owned a barbershop named Jim.

2. He lost the fortune he had accumulated by investing in worthless real estate.

3. All campers were allowed one hour after eating dinner of free time.

4. The junior college offers a two-year program which may be academic or vocational or both for high school graduates.

5. She began to have serious arguments about the friends she had chosen with her implacable parents.

6. Mr. James thanked the audience for the enthusiasm they had displayed as he reached the end of his speech.

7. Ms. Farnsworth gave an interesting account of the many peacetime uses of atomic energy in assembly this morning.

8. Loretta unhappily admitted taking the money after being confronted with the evidence.

9. Many parents of elementary school children watched the struggle to open the Little League to girls with interest.

10. Municipal governments may be forced to refrain from tearing down sound housing by pressure groups from the community.

Avoiding Dangling Modifiers

A modifying phrase or clause must clearly and sensibly modify a word in the sentence. When there is no word that the phrase or clause can sensibly modify, the modifier is said to dangle.

EXAMPLE *Hiking over the mountain trails,* our packs became heavier and heavier.

You realize at once that this sentence does not say what its author intended. There is no word for the phrase *Hiking over the mountain trails* to modify. An introductory phrase like this modifies the noun or pronoun which immediately follows it; yet *packs,* which is the noun immediately following the phrase here, could not hike over mountain trails. Like most danglers, this example may be corrected in one of two ways:

1. By adding to the sentence a word for the phrase to modify:
   Hiking over the mountain trails, we felt our packs becoming heavier and heavier.
2. By changing the phrase to an adverb clause—that is, by adding a subordinating conjunction and a subject and verb to it:
   As we were hiking over the mountain trails, our packs became heavier and heavier.

Danglers usually create a meaning so ridiculous that only the most careless writer would fail to recognize and correct them. Introductory phrases containing a present participle are the most common dangling modifiers. Before attempting the exercise in this lesson, study the following examples.

NOT CLEAR	Standing behind the catcher, a foul ball struck the umpire.
CLEAR	Standing behind the catcher, the umpire was struck by a foul ball.
CLEAR	A foul ball struck the umpire while he was standing behind the catcher.
NOT CLEAR	While telephoning in the office, the noise confused me.
CLEAR	While telephoning in the office, I was confused by the noise.
CLEAR	The noise confused me while I was telephoning in the office.
NOT CLEAR	Finally realizing the futility of our efforts, the task was abandoned.
CLEAR	Finally realizing the futility of our efforts, we abandoned the task.
CLEAR	When we finally realized the futility of our efforts, we abandoned the task.

EXERCISE In the space below each of the following sentences, indicate how you would revise the sentence to avoid the dangling modifier. As shown by the examples, you need not write the whole sentence. A few of the sentences do not contain danglers. Simply write "clear" in the space after these correct sentences. (Add 10 points for each correctly handled sentence.)

A. While fighting with my brother, ~~two ashtrays and a vase were knocked from the table.~~ *I knocked two ashtrays and a vase from the table.*

B. After joining a neighborhood political group, ~~his interest in local politics increased.~~ *he found that his interest in local politics increased.*

1. Although professing strong religious beliefs, she did not try to force her ideas on other people............................

2. After listening carefully to both sides of the case, the decision of the judge surprised us............................

3. Bolstering each other's courage with confident remarks, we literally talked ourselves into braving the storm............................

4. When addressing an audience of high school students, their alternating periods of quiet and restlessness tell you how interesting or uninteresting you are............................

5. Being naturally diffident, entering a new school was a painful experience for him............................

6. Convicted of selling narcotics, the judge sentenced him to life imprisonment............................

7. Not amused by their teacher's flood of facetious remarks, the class came close to open rebellion............................

8. By explaining her problem, I understood better what was worrying her.
....

9. Having been for many years the leading reactionary in the Senate, the

voters finally retired him to private life.........................

....

10. Through following a prescribed diet and taking regular injections of insulin, a diabetic may lead a normal life.........................

....

Building Vocabulary

affluent /áf lū ənt/, *adj.* Rich, prosperous: *An affluent woman, she spent her money freely.* —**affluence**, *n.* Wealth, abundance.

apathy /áp ə thē/, *n.* Lack of emotion, feeling, or excitement; lack of concern with things which usually arouse feeling: *Ms. Stone's apathy toward her job brought about her dismissal.*—**apathetic** /áp ə thét-ik/, *adj.*

connive /kə nív/, *v.* To cooperate secretly with someone; to have a secret understanding with someone: *Three members of the team had connived to lose the game. If you do not tell the police what you saw, you are conniving in the theft of the car.*—**connivance** /kə ní vəns/, *n.*

exonerate /ig zón ə rāt/, *v.* To free someone from blame or from an accusation: *After hearing my story, the council exonerated me.*

incongruous /in kóng grū əs/, *adj.* Having inconsistent or inharmonious parts; lacking consistency or harmony: *It seemed incongruous that a star athlete should be afraid of a hypodermic needle.*—**incongruity** /ín kong grū ə tē/, *n. The most ridiculous incongruity* in the movie was the sad music played during the happy ending.

inexorable /in ék sər ə bə-l/, *adj.* Unyielding; not changeable; not persuadable; relentless: *We are all victims of the inexorable process called aging.*

plaintiff /plán tif/, *n.* One who brings a lawsuit against another. Antonym: *defendant: The lawyer for the plaintiff thought she had a strong case for damages, but the judge ruled in favor of the defendant.*

proximity /prok sím ə tē/, *n.* Nearness to something: *Our proximity to the movie screen made the picture seem blurry to us.*

sagacity /sə gás ə tē/, *n.* Mental keenness, shrewdness: *Crooked lawyers fear Judge Lee's sagacity.*—**sagacious** /sə gā shəs/, *adj. My new employer was a kind and sagacious man.*

sanguine /sáng gwin/, *adj.* Hopeful, cheerful: *The therapist's sanguine view of her chances made her work harder than ever to walk again.*

EXERCISE In the blank at the right of each line, write a synonym or short definition of the italicized word. Look back only if you cannot recall the meaning. (Add 10 points for each correct answer.)

1. an *affluent* relative ....

2. *connive* with the enemy ....

3. a *sanguine* outlook ....

4. the *inexorable* process of the law ....

5. an *apathetic* class ....

6. *exonerated* by the facts ....

115

7. a peculiar *incongruity* ....

8. sympathy for the *plaintiff* ....

9. an amazing *sagacity* ....

10. in dangerous *proximity* ....

In the blank at the right of each word, write the form of the word that would be correct for the part of speech specified. (Add 20 points for each correct answer.)

A. veracious   noun   *veracity*

1. affluent   noun   ....   4. sagacity   adj.   ....

2. apathetic   noun   ....   5. connive   noun   ....

3. incongruity   adj.   ....

REVIEW EXERCISE   Fill each blank in the following passage with the appropriate word from the list which precedes the passage. (Add 4 points for each correct answer.)

amenable	connive	impervious	latent	pecuniary
apathetic	deprecated	irrevocable	opulent	reiterated

My parents had always (1)............. my desire for a car. No matter how often I (2)............. my request, they would remind me that their minds were made up, that their decision was (3)............. Our family, they would say, could not live in a(n) (4)............. way, as if it had money to burn. Since they had usually been (5)............. to my smaller requests, I was surprised to find them (6)............. to my pleading for a cheap used car.

My friend Ann Novak's hitherto (7)............. desire for a car began to show itself last spring. Ann's family was somewhat (8)............. toward the whole idea; Ann could have a car, they said, if she could surmount certain (9)............. barriers. Upon learning this, I suggested that we (10)............. to acquire a car in joint ownership, without letting my parents know the arrangement.

Follow the direction above for the remainder of the exercise.

abstain	ambiguous	exonerated	lucrative	pernicious
adamant	assiduous	feasible	obsequious	precarious
affluent	augment	immaculate	obsolete	proximity

By pooling our savings we made a down payment on an ancient but not yet

(11)............... compact which Wilson Dorn had for sale at his service station. Ann put the motor in good condition, and I applied water and wax until the exterior was (12)............... and shiny. Buying the car in Ann's name (13)............... me from the charge of disobeying my parents, and the (14)............... of Ann's home to mine made dual ownership (15)............... Ann and I soon learned, however, of the pursuit of a creditor named Wilson. We took after-school jobs at his service station to (16)............... our resources. We behaved in a shamefully (17)............... manner in order to please him and were the most (18)............... laborers he had.

Finally my parents gave in and bought me a car, which they presented with the stipulation that I must pay for its upkeep. Now I was indeed in a(n) (19)............... position. I not only had to maintain my own car but also had six more payments to share on Ann's and mine, and Ann was (20)............... in her insistence that I stand by my bargain with her. I was rescued from this terribly (21)............... situation when Ann's parents heard the whole story from Wilson and, feeling somewhat more (22)............... than usual, paid up our debts and gave our car to Ann. Henceforth I shall (23)............... from the (24)............... habit of buying on the installment plan until I have a more (25) .... job than washing cars.

Giving Pronouns Clear Antecedents

The antecedent of a pronoun is the word or group of words to which the pronoun refers.

In the following sentences, the pronouns are underscored, and their antecedents are printed in red.

I wrote to the **manager**, but he did not reply.
Pointing to the **rolls**, Mrs. Cobb said, "One dozen of these, please."
Religion is not only a belief; it is a way of life.
I will get the **books** which you recommend.

Since the meaning of a pronoun is clear only if the reader knows the pronoun's antecedent, a writer must make sure every pronoun used has a clear antecedent.

1. Ambiguous Reference The reference of a pronoun is ambiguous if it is not clear to which of two possible antecedents the pronoun refers.

AMBIGUOUS   Madeline told Jean that Carolyn didn't remember *her*.

The pronoun *her* is ambiguous because it may refer to either Madeline or Jean. One way of making the sentence clear is to use a direct quotation.

CLEAR   Madeline said to Jean, "Carolyn didn't remember **me**."
ALSO CLEAR   Madeline said to Jean, "Carolyn didn't remember **you**."

2. General Reference The reference of a pronoun is general if the pronoun refers to an idea expressed in a phrase or clause rather than to a single specific antecedent.

GENERAL   Students exhibit bad manners by putting their feet on chairs, throwing papers onto the floor, laughing at other pupils' errors, and racing to the door when the period is over. *It* is just as bad out of the classroom.

The pronoun *it* does not have a clearly stated antecedent. The meaning can be clarified by substituting a noun (with modifiers, when necessary).

CLEAR   **Their manners** are just as bad out of the classroom.

3. Weak Reference The reference of a pronoun is weak if the pronoun refers to an unexpressed antecedent.

WEAK   The heavy snowstorm was beautiful to watch as *they* floated slowly downward.
CLEAR   The heavy snowstorm was beautiful to watch as **the flakes** floated slowly downward.

EXERCISE   The items in this exercise contain pronouns whose antecedents are not clear. Correct the sentences either by crossing out words and writing other words above them or by merely inserting words. (Add 10 points for each correct revision.)

A. Tom had met the football coach in the spring, but ~~he~~ *the coach* did not remember him in September.

B. Students are grouped in classes homogeneously according to ability. This *system* works out fairly well.

1. Telephone the library and ask for the information you want. If you can't get it, tell the operator.

2. The Pony Express had eighty riders and 420 horses, changing them every ten miles.

3. I overheard Helen telling Carmela about her Latin test.

4. After school Joe and I stopped at the bakery and bought some to eat on the way home.

5. For years she struggled against poverty and failure, which undoubtedly affected her health.

6. Many students criticized the Council for its new regulations. I thought they were quite unfair.

7. Because my father is an air force officer, our family has never spent more than three years in one place, and I am tired of it.

8. I enjoy experimenting in the laboratory, but I do not enjoy writing them up afterwards.

9. I refused to listen while Henry deprecated the importance of the work on which I had spent several strenuous weeks. It made me tired.

10. Dr. Bowles cut the girl's clothes from her fractured legs and placed them in temporary splints.

Expressing Parallel Ideas Grammatically

Express parallel ideas in the same grammatical form.

In parallel constructions pair a noun with a noun, a verb with a verb, an infinitive with an infinitive (*to go, to see,* and so on), a participle with a participle, a phrase with a phrase, and a clause with a clause.

Study the following sentences in which the parallel, or "paired," elements are in color.

1. Allan decided that he would rather be a **teacher** than a **doctor**. (nouns)
2. Teachers must **know** their subject matter **thoroughly**, **present** it **interestingly**, and **answer** questions **willingly**. (verbs and adverbs)
3. Counseling will help you **to understand** the problem better and **to solve** it more quickly. (infinitives)
4. Candidates for a scholarship may qualify either by **taking** an examination or by **passing** specified courses. (gerund phrases)
5. Trains **running ahead of schedule** are as great a hazard as trains **running behind schedule**. (participial phrases)
6. I believed not only **that you would do a good job** but **that you would enjoy the work**. (noun clauses)

119

Study the following sentences, noting how the lack of parallelism in the first sentence in each group has been corrected in the second sentence.

NOT PARALLEL   I like *receiving* letters much better than *to write* them. (gerund paired with infinitive)

PARALLEL   I like **receiving** letters much better than **writing** them. (gerund paired with gerund)

NOT PARALLEL   Most of my friends are good *students* as well as *athletic*. (noun paired with adjective)

PARALLEL   Most of my friends are good **students** as well as **athletes**. (noun paired with noun)

NOT PARALLEL   Mr. Thorpe mistakenly thinks all students are *apathetic, indolent, and they behave badly.* (clause paired with adjectives)

PARALLEL   Mr. Thorpe mistakenly thinks all students are **apathetic, indolent,** and **badly behaved**. (adjective paired with adjective)

EXERCISE   Below each of the sentences are two expressions. One of these, if used in the blank space in the sentence, would be parallel in form with another element in the sentence. Write the letter (*a* or *b*) of this expression at the right. (Add 10 points for each correct answer.)

A. The Mayor must decide whether to use the new tax money for better schools or _____.

   a. she should improve the recreation facilities   b. for improved recreation facilities   A. *b.*

1. Tsetse flies are notorious as carriers of the disease nagana in cattle and _____.

   a. they cause sleeping sickness in humans   b. of sleeping sickness in humans   1. . . . . .

2. Tsetse is a name of Bantu origin or _____.

   a. of Hausa origin   b. a Hausa word   2. . . . . .

3. Tsetse flies feed by piercing the skin with their mouth-parts and _____.

   a. they suck the blood of animals and humans   b. by sucking the blood of animals and humans   3. . . . . .

4. A female tsetse fly lives for about six months and _____.

   a. giving birth to no more than twelve larvae   b. gives birth to no more than twelve larvae   4. . . . . .

5. Sleeping sickness is a terrible disease which runs a slow course and _____.

   a. ending in coma and death   b. ends in coma and death   5. . . . . .

6. Some sleeping sickness can be controlled if riverside vegetation is cut down and _____.

   a. if flies are trapped in paths and clearings   b. by trapping flies in paths and clearings   6. . . . . .

7. The flies are attracted by dark colors and ____.
   a. repelled by light   b. white clothing is found   7. . . . . .
      clothing   to repel them
8. Fly screens are useful not only on buildings but also ____.
   a. when you are on a   b. on vehicles   8. . . . . .
      vehicle
9. The disease that attacks cattle is far more difficult to control
   than the disease ____.
   a. that attacks humans   b. attacking humans   9. . . . . .
10. The tsetse fly has retarded the penetration of the African
    jungle and ____.
    a. converting of the land   b. the conversion of the   10. . . . . .
       to agriculture   land to agriculture

Expressing Parallel Ideas in Parallel Form

In parallel constructions repeat an article, a preposition, or a pronoun whenever necessary to make the meaning clear.

Study the following pairs of sentences. Note that the meaning of the second sentence in each pair is different from that of the first. This difference in meaning is due to the inclusion of a word which was omitted from the first sentence.

1. The owner and manager (one person) agreed to buy a full-page ad.
   The owner and *the* manager (two persons) agreed to buy a full-page ad.

2. George gave more time and help to his brother than Jill (did).
   George gave more time and help to his brother than *to* Jill.

3. The mayor declared that the old buildings must be razed, that their occupants must move, and she could not be persuaded to change her mind.
   The mayor declared that the old buildings must be razed, that their occupants must move, and *that* she could not be persuaded to change her mind.

Place correlative conjunctions immediately before the parallel items.

The common correlative conjunctions are *both . . . and, not only . . . but (also), neither . . . nor, either . . . or.* Always used in pairs, these conjunctions introduce parallel items.

Each part of these two-part conjunctions should be placed immediately before the item it introduces.

NONSTANDARD   To escape detection she *both* changed her name *and* her address.

In this sentence "both changed" does not make sense; there is no item parallel with "changed." What the writer meant to say is "changed *both her name and her address.*" Now the correlative conjunctions immediately precede respectively the parallel items *her name* and *her address.*

121

NONSTANDARD	Mrs. Austen *not only* supported the National Organization for Women *but also* her local women's political caucus.
STANDARD	Mrs. Austen supported not only the National Organization for Women but also her local women's political caucus.
NONSTANDARD	Christopher will probably *either* ask Phyllis *or* me to go.
STANDARD	Christopher will probably ask either Phyllis or me to go.
NONSTANDARD	I *neither* approved of his friends *nor* his family.
STANDARD	I approved of neither his friends nor his family.

Include in the second part of a parallel construction all words necessary to make the construction complete.

NONSTANDARD   Pulling crab grass is a harder job than clover.

The fault in this sentence is that *pulling* is compared to *clover*. To make the sentence clear, you must add *pulling* to the second of the parallel terms: *Pulling crab grass is a harder job than pulling clover.*

NONSTANDARD   Bread made with sugar is seldom as good as honey.

STANDARD   Bread made with sugar is seldom as good as that made with honey.

EXERCISE   This exercise contains eight sentences in which the parallelism is faulty and two sentences in which it is correct. Revise the incorrect sentences by crossing out words and inserting words wherever necessary. Place a circle around the number of each correct sentence. (Add 10 points for each correctly marked sentence.)

(A.) Cleo prefers golf to tennis.

B. He ~~not only~~ brought home *not only* a deer but also a brace of pheasants.

C. She believed that her story was better written than the other ~~pupils.~~ *pupils' stories*

1. Knowledge gained from experience is just as important as what the books teach.

2. The company you keep can either make you a good person or your downfall can be brought about by it.

3. We learn best the subjects which interest us and skim over those which do not.

4. Hunting in Canada is different from anywhere else.

5. It's more interesting to me to read adventure stories than working difficult math problems.

6. The people of the Philippines had no more desire to be ruled by the United States than the Spanish.

7. Her parents not only sent her away from home but also refused to give her any money.

8. The four diplomats could neither agree on the time nor the place of their next meeting.

9. I said that if I could have my way, I would neither see him nor his sister again.

10. Her stories are characterized by simple vocabulary, rapid action, and she uses a vast amount of dialogue.

Chapter Review

Improve the structure of the following sentences by inserting words wherever necessary and crossing out unnecessary words. (Add 10 points for each correct sentence.)

A. Having received no word from you, *we changed* our plans ~~were changed~~.

1. The book describes the depression of the 1930's that my father is always talking about very briefly.

2. Rocks are always a menace to boats which can be seen only at low tide.

3. The auditorium of the new school will not only be used by the school, but also the community will use it.

4. While we were helping the librarians stack the books, we noticed that they were in poor condition.

5. To cover the forty miles of old wagon trail, we rented a decrepit jeep from the proprietor of a gas station without a windshield and with a leak in the radiator.

6. When my father owned the grocery store, I used to deliver them for him.

7. Not knowing much about whaling, this book created a new interest for me.

8. Mrs. Okada suggested that I read a book written by Solzhenitsyn for my next book report.

9. At six years of age, his mother gave him his first piano lessons.

10. At home Ralph's duties are to set the table for dinner, wash the dishes, and his room must be kept clean.

DIRECTIONS   Read the following passage carefully. Then answer the multiple-choice questions which follow it. Write the letter of your choice in the space provided after each question. (Add 10 points for each correct answer.)

CHOOSING A COLLEGE

1 The first chance to choose a school for most students comes when they have to choose a college. **2** Their elementary school and high school were chosen for them, they simply went where they were sent. **3** Guidance counselors and parents can help you choose a college, but you yourself have to make the final decision perhaps the most important one you have ever made.

4 There are four factors in choosing a college which must be considered. **5** First, you must decide what kind of college you want. **6** You will have to decide whether you want a small or a large college, a coeducational or a non-coeducational school, a liberal arts or a technical school. **7** Second, you must consider the location. **8** Preferring to study in a different part of the United States, a college in an unfamiliar region is chosen by some students. **9** Some don't like the city, and they choose a college in a small town. **10** Third, you must pick a school that is neither too difficult nor too easy. **11** Finally, find out whether or not the students are the kind you will like at this college. **12** To do so, you may visit the college when it is in session, talk to students who go there, or your guidance counselor may be consulted.

1 In which of the following versions of sentence 1 is the phrase "for most students" most effectively placed?   1. .....
 A The first chance to choose a school for most students . . . (as in the passage)
 B For most students the first chance to choose a school comes when they have to choose a college.
 C The first chance for most students to choose a school comes when they have to choose a college.
 D The first chance to choose a school comes when they have to choose a college for most students.

2 The best punctuation to follow *them* in sentence 2 is   2. .....
 A a comma (as in the passage)   C a period (and capital)
 B a semicolon   D no punctuation

3 If you put the first idea in sentence 3 into a subordinate clause, the best conjunction to begin the clause would be   3. .....
 A If   B Because   C Although   D As

4 The best punctuation to follow *decision* in sentence 3 is   4. .....
 A comma   C semicolon
 B period (and capital)   D no punctuation

5 Which of the following versions of sentence 4 is most effective?

5. . . . . .

   A There are four factors in choosing a college which must be considered. (as in the passage)

   B There are four factors which must be considered in choosing a college.

   C The factors in choosing a college which must be considered are four.

   D Four factors must be considered in choosing a college.

6 Of the following versions of sentence 8, which is the clearest?

6. . . . . .

   A Preferring to study in a different part of the United States, a college in an unfamiliar region is chosen by some students. (as in the passage)

   B Some students, preferring to study in a different part of the United States, choose a college in an unfamiliar region.

   C Some students choose a college in an unfamiliar region who prefer to study in a different part of the United States.

   D Choosing a college in an unfamiliar region, some students prefer to study in a different part of the United States.

7 In which of the following versions of sentence 9 is the relationship of ideas most clearly expressed?

7. . . . . .

   A Some don't like the city, and they choose a college in a small town. (as in the passage)

   B Some don't like the city, choosing a college in a small town.

   C A college in a small town is chosen by some who don't like the city.

   D Because they don't like the city, some choose a college in a small town.

8 In which of the following versions of sentence 10 are the parallel elements handled correctly?

8. . . . . .

   A Third, you must pick a school that is neither too difficult nor too easy. (as in the passage)

   B Third, you must pick a school that neither is too difficult nor easy.

   C Third, you must neither pick a school that is too difficult nor that you will find too easy.

   D Third, you must pick a school that is neither too difficult nor that you will find too easy.

9 In which of the following versions of sentence 11 is the phrase "at this college" properly placed?   9. . . . . .

    A Finally, find out whether or not the students are the kind you will like at this college. (as in the passage)

    B Finally, find out whether or not at this college the students are the kind you will like.

    C Finally, find out whether or not the students at this college are the kind you will like.

    D Finally, find out at this college whether or not the students are the kind you will like.

10 The final part of sentence 12 will be parallel in form with the rest of the sentence if it is changed to: 10. . . . . .

    A or by consulting your guidance counselor.

    B or through consultation with your guidance counselor.

    C or consult your guidance counselor.

    D or consulting your guidance counselor.

LESSON 54

Building Vocabulary

disparage /dis pár ij/, *v.* To lower the estimation of someone or something; to speak slightingly of someone or something; *Although I do not approve of Ms. Romano's appointment, I do not disparage her ability.* —**disparaging,** *adj. I objected to her disparaging remarks.*

mundane /mún dān/, *adj.* Worldly, earthly. From the Latin word *mundus,* meaning "world," *mundane* means worldly as opposed to heavenly or spiritual: *She said the church should be concerned with mundane matters as well as with spiritual matters. A ruthless businessman, he seems to be concerned with mundane affairs only.*

nefarious /ni fár ē əs/, *adj.* Very wicked: *A nefarious act must not go unpunished.*

peremptory /pə rémp tər ē/, *adj.* Very positive; not to be refused or denied; dogmatic: *Club members object to the president's peremptory demands.*

posthumous /pós chū məs/, *adj.* Happening after death. As you know, the Latin prefix *post–* means "after": post-season games; post-script; post-mortem. A *posthumous* book is a book published *after the death of* its author: *Stephen Foster, the composer, died in poverty; his fame was posthumous.*

surfeited /súr fit əd/, *adj.* Overfed to the point of nausea; having had too much of something: *After one day behind the soda fountain I was surfeited with ice cream. Surfeited with drills, the team went stale before the big game.*

tacit /tás it/, *adj.* Silent, unspoken: *Her refusal to speak against the measure in the Senate was interpreted as tacit approval of it. Tacit* is commonly used to mean "implied." The idea in the preceding example is expressed in the cliché, "Silence gives consent." *Lorna and I had a tacit agreement to help each other at all times.*

taciturn /tás ə turn/, *adj.* Not speaking, not talkative. Having learned that *tacit* means *unspoken,* you will recognize how *taciturn* means "not speaking": *A taciturn person is one who says very little. Pete is a taciturn boy; one must guess at his thoughts.*

tenacious /ti nấ shəs/, *adj.* Holding fast or likely to hold fast; stubborn: *A tenacious fighter, she refused to give in.*—**tenacity** /ti nás ə tē/, *n. I admire the tenacity with which Aida clings to her ideals.*

voracious /vau rā shəs/, *adj.* Greedy in eating; very eager; insatiable: *The voracious diners left not a single crumb. A voracious reader, he prefers the company of books to that of people.*

EXERCISE Write on the line before each word the letter of the item from the list at the right which best expresses the word's meaning. (Add 10 points for each correct answer.)

. . . . 1. peremptory
. . . . 2. surfeited
. . . . 3. nefarious
. . . . 4. disparage
. . . . 5. tacit
. . . . 6. voracious
. . . . 7. mundane
. . . . 8. tenacious
. . . . 9. taciturn
. . . . 10. posthumous

a. unspoken
b. worldly
c. happening after death
d. positive
e. wicked
f. not talkative
g. overfed
h. greedy
i. speak slightingly of
j. holding fast

REVIEW EXERCISE Place in the space at the right the letter of the word which is closest in meaning to the italicized word. (Add 5 points for each correct answer.)

1. *incongruous* behavior
   a. improbable b. unreliable c. odd d. sagacious 1. . . . .
2. an *inexorable* doom
   a. uncertain b. unlikely c. painful d. certain 2. . . . .
3. doubtful *propriety*
   a. success b. fitness c. assistance d. technique 3. . . . .
4. *inanimate* articles
   a. unnamed b. worthless c. stationary d. lifeless 4. . . . .
5. an *immutable* plan
   a. secret b. indefinite c. unchanging d. unworkable 5. . . . .
6. *homogeneous* audience
   a. mixed b. male c. all-alike d. responsive 6. . . . .
7. *gregarious* animal
   a. dangerous b. herding c. domestic d. living alone 7. . . . .
8. *expedient* solution
   a. advisable b. brilliant c. facile d. expected 8. . . . .
9. *emulated* by others
   a. achieved b. disparaged c. hindered d. imitated 9. . . . .
10. *candid* reply
    a. calm b. obedient c. frank d. angry 10. . . . .
11. *derogatory* speech
    a. fallacious b. unfavorable c. veracious d. enthusiastic 11. . . . .
12. rule by *coercion*
    a. the people b. force c. two rulers d. persuasion 12. . . . .

13. *dogmatic* statement
    a. thoughtless b. irrevocable c. positive   d. lucid   13. . . . .
14. real *panacea*
    a. compliment b. punishment c. experience d. cure-all   14. . . . .
15. delightfully *affable*
    a. agreeable   b. intimate   c. clever   d. facetious   15. . . . .
16. *mundane* interests
    a. selfish   b. worldly   c. personal   d. spiritual   16. . . . .
17. *nostalgic* letter
    a. friendly   b. unhappy   c. incoherent d. homesick   17. . . . .
18. *sanguine* thoughts
    a. serious   b. evil   c. hopeful   d. hidden   18. . . . .
19. a *nefarious* scheme
    a. dangerous b. clever   c. complex   d. evil   19. . . . .
20. a *taciturn* mood
    a. silent   b. cheerful   c. generous   d. social   20. . . . .

LESSON 55

Spelling: Troublesome Words in Mathematics

Many of the terms you learn and use in mathematics may prove tricky to spell. You should attempt to master the correct spelling of these difficult words, so that you may write them with confidence when you need them.

The troublesome letter or letters in each mathematical term below have been printed in red. (You probably know the meaning of most of these words; however, check a dictionary for any you are unsure of.)

abscissa	infinity
algebra	logarithm
binomial	parallel
calculus	perimeter
circumference	perpendicular
coefficient	pi
decimal	quadratic
diameter	quotient
equation	radius
equilateral	rectangle
exponent	tangent
hypotenuse	trapezoid
trigonometry	

EXERCISE A Choose ten of the mathematical terms taught in this lesson, and use each in a separate sentence that shows understanding of the term. (Add 10 points for each properly used word.)

1. ....

2. ....

3. ....

4. ....

5. ....

6. ....

7. ....

8. ....

9. ....

10. ....

EXERCISE B   Be prepared to write from dictation the twenty-five mathematical terms taught in this lesson.

EXERCISE C   There may be some mathematical terms *not* covered here that cause spelling problems in your class. With someone to record them on the board, make a class list of ten of these additional terms. Copy them into your notebook. They will then be erased from the board. Study the list you copied, and be prepared to write the words from dictation. (Add 10 points for each correctly spelled word.)

1. ....   6. ....

2. ....   7. ....

3. ....   8. ....

4. ....   9. ....

5. ....   10. ....

REVIEW WORDS   Correctly complete the scientific words below by writing the missing letter or letters in the blanks. The meaning of each word is given in parentheses. (Add 10 points for each correctly spelled word.)

1. corpus....... (a cell)

2. ....clone (a storm)

3. ac.......stics (the science of sound)

4. s.......sm.......graph (an instrument for recording the earth's shock waves)

5. mol.......cule (a unit of matter)

6. ion.......sphere (the highest layer of atmosphere)

7. ....ronometer (an extremely accurate clock)

8. fi.......ion   (the splitting of a nucleus)

9. o.......mos.......s   (diffusion through a membrane)

10. amp.......   (a unit of electric current)

Twenty Words   *Pretest—study—retest.* (Add 5 points for each correctly spelled word.)

1. ap pro pri ate	6. de sir a ble	11. ir re sist i ble	16. prop a gan da
2. bat tal ion	7. em pha size	12. lux u ri ous	17. rec om mend
3. colo nel	8. gov ern ment	13. mur mur ing	18. ser geant
4. com par a tive ly	9. im me di ate ly	14. par tic u lar ly	19. thor ough ly
5. cus tom er	10. in ten tion	15. per ma nent	20. un doubt ed ly

Part Three
REVIEWING STANDARD USAGE

Every day you use several kinds of English. For example, you may use slang, which is one kind of English; or you may use certain localisms or regionalisms which color the English of people in your locality but are not widely used elsewhere. When you talk, you use an informal language, repeating the same familiar words, interspersing your speech with slang and perhaps with expressions which your English teacher would mark for correction if you wrote them in a composition. When you write, you use a more formal language, choosing your words carefully, displaying more of your vocabulary, and demonstrating your skill in writing sentences that are clear, correct, and forceful. When you deliver a serious speech before a school assembly, you try to use formal English, but when you exhort your teammates to a greater effort in a close game, you use the English which is appropriate to the playing field. In all these situations, you are using standard English if you speak and write as people who have mastered the conventions of English usage would speak and write under the same circumstances.

KINDS OF ENGLISH

Broadly speaking, there are two kinds of English: *standard* and *nonstandard.* Standard English is the kind of English usage most widely recognized as acceptable. You should avoid nonstandard English which consists typically of expressions that are not used by people who have mastered the conventions of English usage: *it don't, you was, them books, ain't,* and so on.

Standard English is of two kinds—*formal* and *informal.* The meaning of these terms—formal and informal—when applied to language is roughly similar to their meaning when applied to social behavior. Your formal manners, formal dress, and formal English supposedly represent you at your best. In school, you should use standard formal English in term papers, essay answers on examinations, serious compositions, minutes and reports of meetings, and in public speeches of a serious nature. Informal English, which may admit even some slang, is appropriate in writing personal essays, stories, items for the school paper, friendly letters, and in daily conversation. These kinds of English—standard formal, standard informal, and nonstandard—are called *levels of usage.*

STANDARD OR NONSTANDARD?

It is natural to ask how one finds out whether a particular expression is standard or nonstandard. One help, of course, is the dictionary, which frequently classifies words as slang, dialect, or nonstandard. Another help is reference books on usage such as *A Dictionary of Contemporary American Usage* by Bergen Evans and Cornelia Evans and *American Usage: the Consensus* by Roy H. Copperud. Like the dictionary, these books are based on research into the speech and writing of Americans. Your English textbooks, in turn, reflect the usages recorded in these reference books. A third aid is grammar, which is an attempt to describe the language in terms of definitions and rules or laws.

The rules of grammar are a useful but not invariably reliable guide to usage. Grammar describes the system of a language; usage is concerned with appropriate forms of expression. The two are not always the same, because language is a living and growing thing, and life and growth are not always logical. Changes are brought about by the people who use the language, and grammar rules, which can only be stated when the changes have occurred, necessarily come afterward.

Because language is always changing, it is not easy for authorities on usage to tell whether a particular construction, once nonstandard but more and more widely used in formal writing and speaking, has reached the standard level. Many presently standard words were slang at one time. Many usages which are standard today were once nonstandard and vice versa.

For a long time students were taught that the use of *mad* to mean *angry* was nonstandard. Now the word is used in this way so extensively that it is becoming standard informal usage. Practically no one today uses *whom* as the first word in a question unless writing standard formal English; yet not many years ago *whom* was considered the only correct form: *Whom did you go with? Whom do you want?* Such sentences have now become *Who did you go with? Who do you want?* in standard informal English. Whenever you find in the usage chapters of this workbook an explanation of exceptions to the rules for standard usage (see pages 141 and 153), you can be fairly sure that these exceptions are the result of the changes in the language which have occurred over the years.

Another reason why it is not easy to define an expression as standard or nonstandard is that speakers and writers who have mastered the conventions of English usage differ in their use of many expressions. Just as we have liberals and conservatives in politics and education, so we have liberals and conservatives in the use of language.

In dealing with usages which are debatable, your textbook rules keep you on the conservative, the safe, side. The usage rules in Chapters 8, 9, and 10 are the rules for standard formal English. Most of them apply also to standard informal English. Their purpose is to help you avoid nonstandard English and use standard formal English whenever the occasion requires it.

To sum up, as you study the chapters in Part Three, "Reviewing Standard Usage," remember the following facts:

1. Standard English is the English used by people who have mastered the conventions of English usage.

2. The generally recognized usage levels are:
Standard formal
Standard informal
Nonstandard

3. You should use standard English whenever possible; avoid nonstandard English.

4. Because language is constantly changing, doubt may arise as to whether a particular word or expression is on one level or another. To resolve such doubts, consult a dictionary or the most recent reference book on usage.

CHAPTER EIGHT

Making Words Agree

When we say that two words agree in number, we mean that both are singular or both are plural. Verbs agree with their subjects; pronouns agree with their antecedents. In general, you make words agree automatically. You have been doing so all your life. Note how the words printed in red in the following groups change to agree with their subjects or their antecedents (underscored), the words to which they refer.

The <u>mountain</u> **is** north of us.   One **has** snow on **its** peak.

The <u>mountains</u> **are** north of us.   <u>Both</u> **have** snow on **their** peaks.

LESSON 56

Agreement of the Verb with Its Subject

In a few common constructions, even native speakers of English frequently fail to keep the verb in agreement with its subject. These constructions are reviewed on the following pages.

The number of a subject is not usually changed by a phrase following the subject.

Sometimes a plural word in a phrase following a singular subject may mislead you into the error of making the verb agree with this plural word rather than with the singular subject.

NONSTANDARD   The siding *on these houses* are fireproof.   (The verb *are* is incorrectly made to agree with *houses,* which is in the phrase.)

STANDARD   The **siding** *on these houses* **is** fireproof.   (The verb *is* correctly agrees with its subject, *siding.*)

NONSTANDARD   The perpetrator *of these crimes* have not been caught.

STANDARD   The **perpetrator** *of these crimes* **has** not been caught.

Phrases like <u>together with</u>, <u>as well as</u>, <u>accompanied by</u>, <u>in addition to</u>, and <u>including</u> do not, as a rule, affect the number of the subject.

EXAMPLES   The **President,** *together with the Secretary of State and the Chief of Staff,* **was** at the airport.

The running **track,** *as well as the playing field,* **is** covered with water.

The following words are usually singular: <u>each</u>, <u>either</u>, <u>neither</u>, <u>one</u>, <u>everyone</u>, <u>everybody</u>, <u>no one</u>, <u>nobody</u>, <u>anyone</u>, <u>someone</u>, <u>somebody</u>.

EXAMPLES Each *of these suggestions* **has** merit.
Neither *of your arguments* **makes** sense.
One *of the speakers* **was** angry.

A subject preceded by <u>every</u> or <u>many a</u> is singular and takes a singular verb.

EXAMPLES Every *wheelbarrow, wagon, and truck* **was** pressed into service.
Many a *writer of magazine stories* **has** tried to write a novel.

Note that verbs ending in *s* are singular: He *is, was, has, plays,* etc.

EXERCISE Draw a line under the subject in each of the following sentences. You will select the subject more easily if you first cross out prepositional phrases. Draw two lines under the verb which agrees in number with the subject. (Add 10 points for each correctly marked sentence.)

A. <u>Betty</u>, ~~in addition to Pat and Mary,~~ (have, <u><u>has</u></u>) always handed homework in ~~on time~~.

1. This book, as well as those on reserve, (have, has) been very helpful.

2. Each of your projects (need, needs) further work.

3. Either of these students (seem, seems) to be reliable.

4. His feelings, as well as my protest, (was, were) ignored.

5. Which one of you pranksters (is, are) responsible for this outrage?

6. Any one of these essays (make, makes) excellent reading.

7. The sound of drums and bugles (was, were) thrilling.

8. Every ship in both fleets (is, are) fully equipped for the voyage.

9. Membership in such clubs (is, are) usually expensive.

10. Every one of our signals (was, were) understood by the other team.

LESSON 57

Verbs with Compound Subjects; HERE, THERE, WHERE

A compound subject is a subject which consists of two or more connected words which have the same verb. The usual connecting words are *and* and *or*.

EXAMPLES <u>Money</u> **and** <u>fame</u> are elusive goals.
<u>The caretaker</u> **or** <u>the superintendent</u> is responsible.

Most compound subjects joined by and are plural and take a plural verb.

EXAMPLES   January and February are slow months in this business.
Baseball and football were his favorite sports.

Singular subjects joined by or, nor, either . . . or, and neither . . . nor are singular and take a singular verb.

EXAMPLES   Melissa or her sister has the key.
Neither the grocery nor the drugstore was open.

The conjunction *or* joins two or more words, but the conjunction tells the reader to consider each subject separately rather than both together.

When two subjects, one of which is singular and the other plural, are joined by or or nor, the verb agrees with the nearer subject.

EXAMPLES   Neither the work itself nor the long hours appeal to me.

Neither the long hours nor the work itself appeals to me.

When the subject comes after the verb, as in sentences beginning with here, there, and where, be especially careful to determine the subject and make sure that the verb agrees with it.

NONSTANDARD   There was five women in the car.
STANDARD   There were five women in the car.

EXERCISE   Draw one line under the subject or subjects in each of the following sentences. Draw two lines under the verb which agrees in number with the subject. (Add 10 points for each correctly marked sentence.)

1. Neither labor nor management (was, were) willing to compromise.

2. Helen and George, after a long engagement, (was, were) finally married.

3. Both Ed and Wilma (was, were) on the debating team.

4. The strong winds and rough sea (is, are) keeping the fishermen in port.

5. (Where's, Where are) your lecture notes?

6. (There's, There are) only a few articles left to choose from.

7. Neither the counselor nor the secretaries (know, knows) about your transcript.

8. Paula and a friend of hers (is, are) coming.

9. You or she (is, are) most likely to win.

10. Either his parents or her aunt and uncle (intend, intends) to chaperone the party.

136

REVIEW EXERCISE In the following sentences, draw one line under the subject and two lines under the verb which agrees with it. This exercise covers the rules so far studied in this chapter. (Add 10 points for each correctly marked sentence.)

1. Each of the cabinet members (have, has) a different point of view.

2. Every one of the defendant's appeals (have, has) been denied.

3. Games or movies (occupy, occupies) the campers on rainy days.

4. Streets in the warehouse district (is, are) generally deserted at night.

5. (There's, There are) one of the missing wallets.

6. Susan B. Anthony, as well as Elizabeth Cady Stanton, (was, were) engaged in the struggle for woman suffrage.

7. Neither of these medicines (is, are) harmful.

8. Some of the stolen coins (have, has) been recovered.

9. Interest on her investments (augment, augments) her income.

10. Every stop street and red light (hold, holds) you up.

LESSON 58

Building Vocabulary

antipathy /an típ ə thē/, *n.* A dislike of someone or something. *Antipathy* is usually followed by *to* or *toward: My antipathy to him was increased by his attempt to cheat me.*

connotation /kón ə tā shən/, *n.* The suggested or implied meaning of a word or expression beyond its actual meaning. Very often a word or phrase suggests something (its *connotation*) which it does not actually mean. *Skinny* and *slender,* for example, have the same basic meaning, but their connotations are quite different: *I find the connotation of the remark insulting.*—connote /kə nōt/, *v.*

cryptic /kríp tik/, *adj.* Having a hidden meaning; obscure; mysterious. Applied usually to a remark or a piece of writing, *cryptic* means that the remark or the writing is not entirely clear; it is intentionally puzzling: *Her essay is so cryptic that it is almost meaningless to me.*

dilemma /di lém ə/, *n.* A situation in which one must choose between two unsatisfactory alternatives: *Eve was in a dilemma: if she*

kept her job she would have to leave school; if she stayed in school without the job, she would soon run out of money.

exorbitant /ig záur bə tənt/, *adj.* Excessive; beyond what is customary or reasonable: *We liked the quality of her wares but considered the prices exorbitant.*

impeccable /im pék ə bə-l/, *adj.* Faultless: *She is an impeccable housekeeper.*

impotent /ím pə tent/, *adj.* Powerless, not necessarily in a physical sense (*im-* [not] + *potent* [powerful]): *Without good leadership an army is impotent.*

ingenuous /in jén y-ū əs/, *adj.* Frank, sincere, naïve: *Pamela is entirely too ingenuous to be deceitful or crafty. Because Jim was ingenuous, he was easy game for dishonest salespeople.* Do not confuse this word with *ingenious,* which means "clever": *He invented an ingenious device to replace the parachute, but aviators were not ingenuous enough to trust it.*

intangible /in tán jə bə-l/, *adj.* Not capable of being touched; describing an object

137

which is not material (in– [not] + *tangible* [capable of being touched]): *In addition to the money I made from the job, I acquired a number of intangible benefits, such as experience, good will, and a sense of responsibility.* *Intangible* is often used to mean "not definite or clear to the mind."

perfunctory /pər fúngk tər ē/, *adj.* Done mechanically, without thought or interest: *Students recited their lessons in a perfunctory manner.*

EXERCISE Draw a line through each italicized word or group of words in the following sentences and write above it a word from this lesson which will give the same meaning as the expression you crossed out. (Add 5 points for each correct answer.)

1. Trapped by snow in the mountains, ten divisions were completely *lacking in power,* and the allies were left in a serious *situation in which every way out was undesirable.*

2. The young senator did not know the common *mechanical and unthoughtful* answers which politicians often give to reporters; he was still too *openly frank and sincere* to fend off their pernicious questions.

3. She spoke in such a *mysterious, obscure* manner that we could only guess at the broader *suggested meanings* of much that she said.

4. My *extreme dislike of* Mr. Campos was increased by the *excessive* fee he charged for handling my case.

5. She gave me a *mechanical* greeting and made some *obscure* remark about being late for an appointment.

6. She was in a *situation in which no good solution was open to her.*

7. A gentleman with *faultless* manners, he is careful not to show his *dislike of* anyone around him.

8. Some of the words the senator used to describe the legislation had unfavorable *implied meanings,* and reporters were puzzled by her *indefinite or unclear* statement.

9. Handcuffed and guarded, she realized that she was *powerless,* and she *naïvely* asked the police to release her.

10. The results of teaching are so *indefinite* that teachers rarely know exactly what they have accomplished.

11. Louis makes *excessive* demands on his tailor because he requires *flawless* workmanship.

138

Match the twenty words with their correct meanings. Write the letter of the meaning in the space before each word. (Add 5 points for each correct answer.)

.... 1. voracious	a.	unchanging
.... 2. sanguine	b.	not loquacious
.... 3. tenacious	c.	doubtful
.... 4. sagacious	d.	wealthy
.... 5. taciturn	e.	very greedy
.... 6. proximity	f.	repeat
.... 7. surfeited	g.	hopeful
.... 8. affluent	h.	dictatorial
.... 9. nefarious	i.	bold
.... 10. reiterate	j.	satiated
.... 11. apathy	k.	holding fast
.... 12. peremptory	l.	hard-working
.... 13. pecuniary	m.	nearness
.... 14. disparage	n.	wicked
.... 15. immutable	o.	laziness
.... 16. assiduous	p.	to belittle
.... 17. dubious	q.	indifference
.... 18. indolence	r.	easily done
.... 19. facile	s.	shrewd
.... 20. audacious	t.	financial

LESSON 59

Collective Nouns; Words of Amount; WHO, WHICH, THAT

A *collective noun* names a group. Frequently used collective nouns are *army, audience, class, club, committee, crew, crowd, faculty, fleet, flock, group, herd, jury, mob, squadron, staff, swarm, team, troop.*

With a collective noun use a singular verb when thinking of the group as a unit; use a plural verb when thinking of the group as individuals.

EXAMPLES   The audience <u>were</u> taking their seats. (The speaker is thinking of the members of the audience as individuals rather than as a group. The plural pronoun *their* indicates this.)

The audience <u>was</u> unusually large. (The speaker is thinking of the audience as a unit.)

The committee <u>have</u> been arguing among themselves for two hours.

The committee <u>has</u> been in session for two hours.

Words stating amount (time, money, measurement, weight, volume, fractions) are usually singular when the amount is thought of as a unit.

EXAMPLES   Two months <u>is</u> a long vacation.

Five dollars <u>pays</u> all expenses of the trip.

Three pounds of sugar <u>is</u> enough.

When the amount is thought of as several separate units, a plural verb is used.

EXAMPLES   These past two weeks <u>have</u> been hectic.

There <u>are</u> four dollars left over.

The number of the verb that agrees with a relative pronoun (who, which, that) is determined by the number of the word to which the pronoun refers.

EXAMPLES   I bought a car *which* <u>was</u> greatly reduced in price.

I bought one of the cars *which* <u>were</u> greatly reduced in price.

This is the letter *that* <u>was</u> written by Migdalia.

This is one of the letters *that* <u>were</u> written by Migdalia.

EXERCISE   Make each sentence correct by drawing a line through the *incorrect* verb in parentheses. (Add 5 points for each correct answer.)

1. The crew (was, were) talking over the mutiny.

2. These last three months (have, has) been very pleasant.

3. He is one of those people who (thinks, think) only of themselves.

4. Our team (was, were) the best combination we could put together.

5. Twelve dollars (is, are) more than I can afford.

6. I could not get any of the books that (was, were) recommended.

7. Forty miles (is, are) more than an hour's drive on these roads.

8. Twenty minutes (seems, seem) long enough for this job.

9. There (is, are) ten dimes in each row of coins.

140

10. The team (plays, play) together better than they did last year.

11. The clerk said that six pounds of salt (was, were) worth one dollar.

12. She is one of the people who (eats, eat) regularly at that restaurant.

13. Ninety dollars a week (is, are) the regular pay for this work.

14. The decorating committee (has, have) been working in the gym.

15. Three quarts (is, are) our family's daily consumption of milk.

16. Among our students, two thirds (is, are) brought to school by bus.

17. Outside the principal's office (was, were) a worried group of students.

18. A flock of migrating birds (was, were) spotted.

19. Is this one of the books which (was, were) in Grandmother's library?

20. Did you know any of the girls who (was, were) in the car?

Agreement of Pronoun and Antecedent

The antecedent of a pronoun is the word to which the pronoun refers. When the antecedent is singular, the pronoun should be singular. When the antecedent is plural, the pronoun should be plural. In the following sentences the pronouns are printed in red; their antecedents are underscored. Note that they agree in number.

EXAMPLES   Neither of the men gave **his** right name.
Every one of the girls gave me **her** picture.
One of our best hitters has broken **his** thumb.
When a student is late, **he** must go to the office.

Note: When the antecedent may be either masculine or feminine, as in the last two examples above, use the masculine pronoun which is understood to apply to both sexes in *standard formal* writing or speech. When possible, you may want to rewrite the sentence in the plural. Avoid the awkward use of *he or she*.

PLURAL SUBSTITUTE   When students are late, **they** must go to the office.
AWKWARD   When a student is late, *he or she* must go to the office.

While *standard formal* usage still usually requires the agreement of pronoun and antecedent, *informal* usage sanctions the use of plural pronouns (*they, their, them*) with singular antecedents when the intended meaning of the antecedent is clearly plural.

STANDARD INFORMAL   Everyone did **their** best.
STANDARD FORMAL   Everyone did **his** best.
STANDARD INFORMAL   Everybody in camp must write **their** parents once a week.
STANDARD FORMAL   Everybody in camp must write **his** parents once a week.

The inconsistency of this colloquial freedom in the use of a plural pronoun to refer to a singular antecedent need not confuse you. Usage is often inconsistent because it reflects the everchanging use of the language. However, since the purpose of this text is to improve your *standard written English,* follow standard formal practice in doing the exercises.

In determining whether a pronoun's antecedent is singular or plural, keep in mind the following facts which you learned in your study of the agreement of verb and subject.

1. The following words are usually singular: *anybody, each, either, neither, one, everyone, everybody, no one, nobody, anyone, someone, somebody.*
2. The number of a word is not usually affected by a phrase following it.
3. A pair of words joined by *and* is plural.
4. A compound construction consisting of two *singular* words joined by *or* or *nor* is singular.
5. A collective noun may be either singular or plural, depending on whether the writer is thinking of the group or its members.

EXERCISE In each of the following sentences, underline the antecedent and cross out the incorrect pronoun in parentheses. (Add 5 points for each correctly marked sentence.)

1. Each of the girls rode (her, their) own horse.

2. Somebody had apparently done (his, their) best to prevent my leaving.

3. Both Sally and Jean did (her, their) homework in class.

4. The crowd took sides in the debate (it was, they were) watching.

5. A person must save part of (his, their) income.

6. No person can control (his, their) destiny completely.

7. Everyone in the school and a great many townspeople showed (his, their) interest in a shorter school day.

8. Each fan has (their, his) favorite player.

9. Neither Stephanie nor Rosemary will be able to play (her, their) best today.

10. Nature and nature's creatures may one day reveal all (its, their) secrets.

11. You should respect a teacher, for (they, he) can be of great help to you.

12. Anyone who objects to (his, their) grade should consult the teacher.

13. When a student gets bored with school, (he, they) will usually think of an excuse to stay home.

14. Both Pete and he seemed to be at the top of (their, his) game.

15. If anyone objects to this editorial, (he, they) can write to the editor.

16. Neither of the arrested men would tell the reporter (their, his) name.

17. No one on the Village Council would permit (themselves, himself) to be quoted.

18. Mrs. Abernathy and Miss Fuentes will help you with your schedule if you ask (them, her).

19. Every camper must do (his, their) own laundry.

20. As each driver crossed the finish line, (their, his) name was announced.

Chapter Review

If a sentence is correct, write a plus (+) in the space at its right. If a sentence is incorrect, cross out the incorrect word and write the correct form in the space. (Add 5 points for each correctly marked sentence.)

A. Which one of these snakes ~~are~~ poisonous? *is*

B. Neither she nor her friends are innocent. *+*

1. The success of these players are due to their excellent physical condition. . . . .

2. Where's your brother and sister? . . . .

3. Not one of the nations feels antipathy for the others. . . . .

4. One of the old remedies are sulfur and molasses. . . . .

5. Once a person learns to ride a bicycle, they will never forget how to do it. . . . .

6. Neither George nor Paul could do their best under such adverse circumstances. . . . .

7. Some of the crowd were shouting their protests. . . . .

8. A small group of demonstrators was waiting for the mayor. . . . .

9. Neither of the girls saved the money she earned. . . . .

10. The design of these machines are patented. . . . .

11. The cost of labor and materials puts us in a dilemma. . . . .

12. Many a young person has been led astray by their insatiable desire for wealth. . . . .

13. Jane, as well as her brothers, have studied the piano. . . . .

14. A pair of hip boots are necessary for this kind of fishing.   . . . .

15. A box of chocolates were lying on the desk.   . . . .

16. Three weeks is as much time as you may have.   . . . .

17. For short trips the train or the bus is preferable.   . . . .

18. Incongruous as it may seem in an affluent family, every one of the sons worked their way through college.   . . . .

19. Two dollars wasn't enough to pay the exorbitant bill.   . . . .

20. He is one of those people who are always late.   . . . .

DIRECTIONS   Insert punctuation and capital letters in the following passage. Correct all errors in subject-verb agreement by crossing out the incorrect verb and writing the correct form above it. (Add 4 points for each correct answer.)

1 Our ancestors would have reacted incredulously to any suggestion that people could make the weather or that weather could be controlled by people. **2** The fact is however that today the possibilities of weather control is great enough so that nineteen states now have laws governing weather modification. **3** The laws reflect our legislators fears that by inducing rain artificially in one area drought may be caused in another. **4** Seeding clouds with silver iodide particles which is one method of making rain have been a subject of experimentation for over twenty years but the effectiveness of the results are still controversial nevertheless there have been lawsuits. Asking compensation for damage done by the rain makers.

5 Cloud seeding to replenish water in the Catskill Mountain Reservoir which supplies water for New York City drew complaints from a Catskill mountain resort owner who claimed it had a detrimental effect on his business. **6** Some ranchers in western Texas brought suit against a group of farmers who had hired a cloud seeder to lessen danger from hail. **7** The ranchers claim was that the rainmaker had deprived them of it while possibly headed their way.

8 In addition to using scientific methods to make rain or in preventing hailstorms, weather modification experts are working on ways to break up dangerous hurricanes or divert them from coastal areas. **9** There has been however a few cases of hurricane rains that have proved beneficial to drought-stricken areas. **10** People may welcome the scientists' efforts who live on the coast, but farmers may not be altruistic enough to want hurricane rains diverted whose crops are dying from drought. **11** Another problem of interest to weather modifiers are the suppression of lightning. **12** Seven out of ten forest fires in the rocky mountain states are caused by lightning and the annual losses from fires started by lightning in the rockies exceeds $25,000,000.

13 Hoping to determine whether lightning can be controlled through modi-fication of clouds Project skyfire was initiated by the United States forest service. **14** The American meteorological society states that, while all current attempts at weather modification are only experimental and relatively ineffec-tive, they do not rule out the possibility that large scale weather modification may become possible in the future.

15 This possibility raises very serious problems. Since weather modification for the benefit of one country may prove harmful to another. **16** Thus the matter becomes international and political as well as something scientists are concerned with.

DIRECTIONS Answer the following multiple-choice questions about the passage you have just read. Write the letter of the best choice in the space at the right. (Add 10 points for each correct answer.)

1 Which of the following versions of the last part of sentence 1 handles the parallel elements, most smoothly?   1. . . . . .
  A that people could make or they could control the weather
  B that people could make the weather or control it
  C that people could make or control the weather

2 Which of the following revisions best corrects the dangling construction in sentence 3?   2. . . . . . .
  A by inducing rain artificially in one area there may be drought in another
  B by inducing rain artificially in one area rain makers may cause drought in another
  C by inducing rain artificially in one area in another drought may result

3 Which of the following versions of the last part of sentence 5 has the best substitute for the vague pronoun *it*?   3. . . . . .
  A who claimed the resulting deluge had a detrimental effect on his business
  B who claimed the deluge which the cloud seeding produced as a result had a detrimental effect on his business
  C who claimed this had a detrimental effect on his business

4 Which of the following versions of the last part of sentence 7 is clearest?   4. . . . . .
  A that the rainmaker had deprived them of it when possibly headed their way

    B that the rainmaker had deprived them of what was possibly headed their way

    C that the rainmaker had deprived them of rain which was possibly headed their way

5 In which of the following is the parallelism in sentence 8 best expressed?   5. . . . . .

    A In addition to using scientific methods to make rain or to prevent hailstorms

    B In addition to using scientific methods to make rain or for the prevention of hailstorms

    C In addition to using scientific methods in making rain or to prevent hailstorms

6 In which of the following revisions of sentence 10 are the subordinate clauses properly placed?   6. . . . . .

    A People may welcome the scientists' efforts who live on the coast, but farmers whose crops are dying from drought may not be altruistic enough to want hurricane rains diverted.

    B People who live on the coast may welcome the scientists' efforts, but farmers whose crops are dying from drought may not be altruistic enough to want hurricane rains diverted.

    C People who live on the coast may welcome the scientists' efforts, but farmers may not be altruistic enough to want hurricane rains diverted whose crops are dying from drought.

7 Which of the following is the most successful way of correcting the error in sentence 13?   7. . . . . .

    A Hoping to determine whether lightning can be controlled through modification of clouds the initiation of Project skyfire was done by the United States forest service.

    B Hoping to determine whether lightning can be controlled through the modification of clouds a project called skyfire was initiated by the United States forest service.

    C Hoping to determine whether lightning can be controlled through the modification of clouds the United States forest service initiated Project skyfire.

8 Which of the following most clearly shows the relationship of ideas in sentence 12?   8. . . . . .

    A *Although* seven out of ten forest fires in the rocky mountain states are caused by lightning, the annual losses from fires started by lightning in the rockies exceeds $25,000,000.

B *Since* seven out of ten forest fires, etc. (as in A)

C *While* seven out of ten forest fires, etc. (as in A)

9. Which of the following is the clearest substitute for the ambiguous pronoun *they* in sentence 14?   9. . . . . .

   A *the attempts* do not rule out the possibility . . .

   B *this* does not rule out the possibility . . .

   C *the Society* does not rule out the possibility . . .

10. Which of the following is the best handling of the parallel items in sentence 16?   10. . . . . .

   A Thus the matter becomes international and political as well as scientific.

   B Thus the matter becomes international and political as well as scientifically interesting.

   C Thus the matter becomes international and political as well as a problem for scientists.

Building Vocabulary

circumspect /súr kəm spect/, *adj.* Considering all angles of a situation before taking any action; careful. The Latin derivation of this word shows clearly its exact meaning: *circum–* (around) + *spicere* (to look) = "to look around." A *circumspect* person is one who, before acting, carefully looks at all possible results of the action: *Because she is usually circumspect in whatever she does, she can be relied on to avoid serious mistakes.*

malevolent /mə lév ə lənt/, *adj.* Wishing evil; showing ill will (Latin *male* [ill] + *volens* [wishing]): *Hitler was a malevolent dictator.* Antonym: *benevolent* (*bene* [well] + *volens*): *She tried to hide her malevolent intentions behind seemingly benevolent acts.*

   The next two words in this lesson are based upon the same Latin word, *male*, meaning "evil, ill."

malicious /mə lísh əs/, *adj.* Evil; arising from evil intentions; hurtful to others: *Out of jealousy, he circulated malicious rumors about his rival.*

malign /mə lín/, *v.* To speak evil of someone or something: *I didn't mind when she maligned me because I knew no one would believe her.* As an adjective, *malign* is a synonym of *malevolent*: *We feared the malign designs of such a cruel man.*

officious /ə físh əs/, *adj.* Offering help or advice which has not been asked for; meddling in others' business: *We grudgingly paid attention to the officious freshman who barged into the senior room.*

ostracize /ós trə sīz/, *v.* To banish from society or from social privileges: *She became so officious that even her best friends ostracized her.*

plagiarize /plā jə ríz/, *v.* To pass off as one's own the work (ideas, writing, etc.) of someone else: *He handed in an essay which had obviously been plagiarized from a recent magazine.*—**plagiarism**,*n.* The act of plagiarizing.

pseudo /sū dō/, *adj.* False, counterfeit, pretended: *The restaurant bore an air of pseudo rusticity.* *Pseudo–* is sometimes used as a combining form meaning "fake" or "false." A *pseudonym* (*pseudo–* [false] + *nym* [name]) is a false name; some authors use a *pseudonym* rather than their real name.

recalcitrant /ri kál sə trənt/, *adj.* Stubbornly resisting authority; disobedient: *The principal asked that only the most recalcitrant pupils be sent to her.*

vindictive /vin dík tiv/, *adj.* Having a strong desire for revenge; revengeful: *Unable to forget my insult, he adopted a vindictive attitude toward me.*

EXERCISE Provide a synonym or definition of the italicized word. (Add 5 points for each correct answer.)

1. a *malevolent* ruler ....

2. a *plagiarized* poem ....

3. a *recalcitrant* child ....

4. those *malicious* words ....

5. *circumspect* behavior ....

6. an *officious* manner ....

7. cruelly *ostracized* ....

8. *maligned* by the newspapers ....

9. *pseudoclassic* architecture ....

10. a *vindictive* spirit ....

Each numbered blank represents one of the ten words in this lesson. Write the appropriate word in each blank.

a. (11)................... by his enemies and (12)....................
by his friends, he became more and more bitter.

b. A teacher should never adopt a(n) (13).............. attitude in order
to get revenge on students who are so (14).............. that they will
do nothing the teacher asks of them.

c. By revealing the fact that most of Professor Lloyd's ideas had been
(15).................. from the writings of others, the critics showed
her to be, after all, only a (16).................. critic.

d. We knew he was (17)............ after he had wished failure upon us,
yet we did not realize until later what (18)............ actions he could
perform.

e. Had she taken the time to work out her plans in a more (19).........
.... fashion, she would not have been so (20)..................
in her direction of the affairs of others.

REVIEW EXERCISE Place in the space at the right the letter of the word which is
opposite in meaning to the italicized word. (Add 10 points for each correct answer.)

1. his *perfunctory* explanation
   a. mechanical   b. candid   c. thorough   d. eccentric   1. .....

2. *mundane* thoughts
   a. spiritual   b. practical   c. coherent   d. worldly   2. .....
3. great *sagacity*
   a. wisdom   b. metropolis   c. sympathy   d. stupidity   3. .....
4. her *diffident* approach
   a. unexpected   b. hesitant   c. bold   d. unusual   4. .....
5. *deprecate* the performance
   a. criticize   b. repeat   c. cancel   d. approve   5. .....
6. an *ingenuous* question
   a. simple   b. harmless   c. deceitful   d. unclear   6. .....
7. *tacit* agreement
   a. irrevocable   b. oral   c. silent   d. unspoken   7. .....
8. comforting *proximity*
   a. nearness   b. guesswork   c. treatment   d. remoteness   8. .....
9. *impeccable* behavior
   a. faulty   b. foolish   c. kind   d. surprising   9. .....
10. *ambiguous* comments
   a. rude   b. cruel   c. clear   d. thoughtful   10. .....

LESSON 63

Spelling: Troublesome Words in Music

Most of the words used in the field of music are foreign loan words. Some come from Latin, some from French, many from Italian, and a few from other languages. Because these words are loan words, their sound-spelling relationships usually follow those of the languages in which they originated. They may therefore present spelling problems to English-speaking people who want to write them.

You probably know the meaning of most of the musical terms below. (Check a dictionary for any that are unfamiliar to you.) The letters that usually cause spelling difficulties are printed in red.

ballet	oboe
baritone	octave
basso	orchestra
cello	percussion
choir	prima donna
clarinet	quartet
concerto	saxophone
cymbal	serenade
ensemble	tenor
impresario	xylophone

EXERCISE A Be prepared to write from dictation the words taught in this lesson.

EXERCISE B Choose ten words from the twenty just taught and use each in a separate sentence that shows understanding of the term. (Add 10 points for each properly used word.)

1. ....
2. ....
3. ....
4. ....
5. ....
6. ....
7. ....
8. ....
9. ....
10. ....

EXERCISE C Study the names of these famous composers. Be prepared to write them from dictation. The difficult spelling spots in each have been printed in red. (Add 5 points for each correctly spelled name.)

1. Bach	6. Brahms	11. Mozart	16. Schumann
2. Bartok	7. Chopin	12. Prokofiev	17. Shostakovich
3. Beethoven	8. Debussy	13. Puccini	18. Strauss
4. Bellini	9. Grieg	14. Rachmaninoff	19. Stravinsky
5. Berlioz	10. Handel	15. Schubert	20. Verdi

REVIEW EXERCISE Correctly complete the mathematical terms below by writing the missing letter or letters in the blanks. (Add 10 points for each correctly spelled word.)

1. radi.......s
2. dec.......m.......l
3. alg.......bra
4. para.......e.......
5. hypot.......nuse

6. expon.......nt
7. ab.......issa
8. calcul.......s
9. trap.......zoid
10. binom.......l

Twenty Words *Pretest—study—retest.* (Add 5 points for each correctly spelled word.)

1. ac com mo date	6. cour te ous	11. fi er y	16. par lia ment
2. an ni hi late	7. de scend ant	12. in oc u late	17. pic nick ing
3. aux il ia ry	8. ec sta sy	13. ma neu ver	18. pos sess
4. com plex ion	9. ef fi cient	14. mis chie vous	19. pro nun ci a tion
5. cor dial ly	10. fas ci nat ing	15. no tice a ble	20. vi cin i ty

151

CHAPTER NINE

Using Pronouns Correctly

For many people personal pronouns are usage troublemakers. These people have never learned whether a certain construction calls for *I* or *me, she* or *her, who* or *whom*. If you find you are not always sure which pronoun form to use, you may eliminate your uncertainty by studying this chapter carefully.

Personal pronouns present problems because they have different forms, and a speaker must learn when to use each form. A pronoun used as the subject of a verb is different in form from a pronoun used as the object of a verb. When used to show possession, a pronoun has still another form. These forms, which are determined by the way the pronoun is used, are called *cases* or case forms. The three cases are the *nominative,* the *objective,* and the *possessive*.

LESSON 64

Using Nominative Pronouns

Learn the nominative personal pronouns[1] so that you can say them quickly from memory.

NOMINATIVE CASE

Singular	Plural
I	we
he	they
she	

The subject of a verb is in the nominative case.

When a pronoun is used by itself as the subject of a verb, it usually does not present a problem, but when it is part of a compound subject (two or more subjects joined by *and, or,* or *nor*), it often does present a problem. Many persons who would not say "*Me* went to the play" will make the mistake of saying "*Lola and me* went to the play." *Lola and me* is a compound construction.

To determine the correct pronoun in a compound construction, try each subject separately. Your ear will tell you the correct form of the pronoun.

NONSTANDARD   Neither Stuart nor *him* is a good hitter. (When you try the pronoun alone—*him* is a good hitter—you recognize the error at once.)

STANDARD   Neither Stuart nor **he** is a good hitter.

[1] The personal pronouns *you* and *it* do not change their forms; therefore they are omitted from this list.

© 1977 HBJ

A predicate nominative is in the nominative case.

A predicate nominative is a noun or pronoun which follows a linking verb (usually a form of *be*) and means the same thing as the subject of the verb.

EXAMPLE   The best <u>player</u> is she.

In this sentence *she* is the predicate nominative. It follows a form of the verb *be* (*is*) and means the same thing as the verb's subject (*player*). *Player* and *she* are the same person.

VERBS		NOMINATIVE PRONOUNS
am		I
is, are	are	he
was, were	followed	she
verbs ending in *be* or *been*	by	we
		they

EXAMPLES   The <u>women</u> on the aisle were they.
The <u>boy</u> in the white sweater must be he.

Modern informal usage accepts the objective pronoun *me* as a predicate nominative. *It's me* may be used instead of the standard formal form *It is I*. Standard formal usage, however, still requires the nominative form of the *other* pronouns after a form of *be: It is he, It is she,* etc. In informal usage, such expressions as *It is him, It is her,* etc., although contrary to rule, are becoming more common, but they have not yet become standard formal English. You are expected to use standard formal English in the exercises in this book and in your written assignments.

EXERCISE   In the space before each sentence, write the letter (*a* or *b*) to show how the pronoun is used. Then draw a line through the incorrect one of the pronouns in parentheses. (Add 4 points for each correct sentence.)

a. subject of verb   *b.* predicate nominative

.... 1. Betty and (she, her) were ostracized by the club.

.... 2. You and (me, I) have been accused of plagiarism.

.... 3. The new president will be either you or (she, her).

.... 4. Are you sure it was (they, them)?

.... 5. Pat and (he, him) have been taking dancing lessons.

.... 6. It might have been (she, her).

.... 7. (She, Her) and I have always feared her vindictive nature.

.... 8. That was (he, him) in the cooking class.

.... 9. That must have been either her sister or (she, her).

. . . . 10. Mrs. Ortiz and (us, we) sophomores built the stage scenery. (To determine the correct form of the pronoun in this kind of construction, omit the word after the pronoun—*sophomores*.)

. . . . 11. Miguel and (I, me) applied for the same job.

. . . . 12. How can (we, us) girls be of help to you?

. . . . 13. The bus driver will be either Andy or (she, her).

. . . . 14. Was the writer of the note you or (she, her)?

. . . . 15. Molly and (she, her) are too circumspect to be officious.

. . . . 16. Leon and (they, them) came in the same car.

. . . . 17. Maria and (I, me) spent the rainy afternoon at the movies.

. . . . 18. If you and (we, us) are late, we'll be very unpopular.

. . . . 19. Are you sure it was (he, him)?

. . . . 20. Could it have been (they, them)?

. . . . 21. Their alibi convinced me that it couldn't have been either Winston or (he, him).

. . . . 22. I thought you and (I, me) were good friends.

. . . . 23. If anyone objects, it will probably be (her, she).

. . . . 24. (Her, She) and (I, me) came home early.

. . . . 25. The two tenors were Bart and (he, him).

LESSON 65

Using Objective Pronouns

The objective personal pronouns are *me, him, her, us, them.* Use the objective pronouns for objects of a verb and objects of a preposition.

The object of a verb is in the objective case.

The object of a verb receives the action expressed by the verb or shows the result of the action.

EXAMPLES   I helped him.   She gave me a bit of advice.[1]

The object of a verb may be compound.

EXAMPLES   She did not expect both Jake and him.

I would not trust either him or her.

---

[1] In this sentence *me* is an indirect object of the verb, and *bit* is a direct object. This distinction is not important, since the case is objective in both instances.

© 1977 HBJ

The object of a preposition is in the objective case.

The object of a preposition is the noun or pronoun which concludes the prepositional phrase. This word is the object of the preposition which begins the phrase.[1]

EXAMPLES   for him (*him* is the object of *for*)   to her (*her* is the object of *to*)

The object of a preposition may be compound.

EXAMPLES   She sent for you and her.

My letter was from my brother and him.

To determine the correct pronoun in a compound construction, try each object separately.

PROBLEM   The book was written by Miss Hellas and (he, him).

If you omit *Miss Hellas* and try the pronoun separately, your ear will probably tell you that *him* is correct:

The book was written by him.   (not *he*)

PROBLEM   Do you think Marilyn looks like (she, her) or (I, me)?

Try each object separately:

Do you think Marilyn looks like her?   (not *she*)
Do you think Marilyn looks like me?   (not *I*)

STANDARD   Do you think Marilyn looks like her or me?

EXERCISE   In the space before each sentence, write the letter (*c* or *d*) to show how the pronoun is used. Then cross out the incorrect one of the two pronouns in parentheses. (Add 10 points for each correct sentence.)

c. object of verb (direct or indirect)
d. object of preposition

.... 1. She is depending on you and (us, we).

.... 2. She sent Arlene and (I, me) a copy of her book.

.... 3. Were you named after your father or (he, him)?

.... 4. I was standing in line behind Ethel and (her, she).

.... 5. Don't tell Ernest and (them, they) how we maligned them.

.... 6. A recalcitrant child, she will obey neither her parents nor (we, us).

.... 7. Have you seen Eugene or (he, him)?

.... 8. Does that malicious remark refer to Yvonne or (me, I)?

.... 9. He left a cryptic message for you and (her, she).

.... 10. The lifeguards rescued both Alec and (him, he).

[1]For a list of prepositions, see page 13.

REVIEW EXERCISE In each of the following sentences you are given a choice between two pronouns, one of which is nominative, the other objective. Make your choice on the basis of the uses you have just studied. Write in the space at the left the corresponding letter from the four uses listed below. Decide whether the nominative or objective form is called for, and draw a line through the incorrect one of the two pronouns in parentheses. (Add 5 points for each correct sentence.)

WAYS PRONOUNS ARE USED

a. subject of verb	nominative forms:
b. predicate nominative	*I, he, she, we, they*
c. object of verb	objective forms:
d. object of preposition	*me, him, her, us, them*

a. A. Hilda and (she, ~~her~~) will arrive on Monday.

d. B. The card is addressed to you and (~~I,~~ me).

.... 1. You and (I, me) will be partners.

.... 2. Ask for Cruz or (him, he).

.... 3. That is (him, he).

.... 4. (Him, He) and (I, me) won easily.

.... 5. Don't tell Earl and (she, her).

.... 6. She invited the Skavinskis and (we, us).

.... 7. The heat was too much for Hal and (me, I).

.... 8. I'm sure it was (they, them).

.... 9. Sally and (he, him) made disparaging remarks about the school.

.... 10. The leaders will be Juanita and (she, her).

.... 11. Patrick and (they, them) were late.

.... 12. They clung tenaciously to Anthony and (he, him).

.... 13. The principal exonerated Amy and (me, I).

.... 14. It might have been (he, him).

.... 15. Steve and (she, her) would never connive in that nefarious plan.

.... 16. I was sitting behind Joan and (he, him).

.... 17. Take Henrietta and (her, she) with you.

.... 18. He called Rick and (we, us) to the office.

.... 19. I was looking for you and (they, them).

.... 20. It could be either you or (she, her).

Building Vocabulary

culpable /kúl pə bə-l/, *adj.* Deserving blame; blameworthy. People are *culpable* when they do something for which they may be rightly criticized or condemned: *If you help Leona to cheat on an examination, you are as culpable as she.*

ostensible /os tén sə bə-l/, *adj.* Apparent, pretended. Most of us occasionally try to cover up the real reason for an act by giving a false reason. This pretended reason is an *ostensible* reason. Usually it is meant to mislead others: *The ostensible reason for his absence was his father's poor health; actually, he went to the ball game.*—**ostensibly**, *adv. Lonnie went to Shelley's house, ostensibly to get help on his homework; of course, that was only the ostensible reason.*

platitude /plát ə tūd/, *n.* A commonplace, trite remark. People whose conversations are full of *platitudes* are dull conversationalists. They simply say things that everyone has heard many times before. "Better be safe than sorry" is one kind of platitude: *We were bored by Gloria's assembly speech because it was just a series of platitudes.*

replete /ri plḗt/, *adj.* Filled to capacity. Usually followed by *with* (*replete with*). *Replete* sometimes is a synonym for *satiated* or *surfeited: I am replete with good food; in fact, I wish I hadn't eaten so much. His conversation is replete with platitudes.*

salient /sā lē ənt/, *adj.* Standing out; prominent; conspicuous: *Organize your writing so that the reader can grasp the salient points you are trying to make.*

scrupulous /skrū́ pyə ləs/, *adj.* Very careful to do the right thing; giving conscientious attention to details: *The teacher praised Elena for the scrupulous way she did her assignment.*—**scrupulously**, *adv. His room is always scrupulously clean.* Antonym: *unscrupulous*—Not morally right; not conscientious: *His fortune was made through a series of unscrupulous business deals. She was sent to prison for her unscrupulous treatment of those who had entrusted their money to her.*

spurious /spy-ūr ē əs/, *adj.* Not genuine; false: *We escaped because the border guard did not detect the fact that our passports were spurious.*

subjugate /súb jū gāt/, *v.* To conquer; to subdue; to force into one's power: *To subjugate the people is more difficult than to defeat their armies.*

transitory /trán sə táur ē/, *adj.* Lasting only a short time; temporary: *Knowing that the pain was transitory, she was better able to endure it.*

venerable /vén ər ə bə-l/, *adj.* Deserving respect or admiration. *Venerable* is used in referring to the old: *The entire village considered my grandfather to be a venerable gentleman.*—**veneration**, *n. Pablo Casals was held in deep veneration.*

EXERCISE Before each numbered word, write the letter of its synonym. (Add 10 points for each correct answer.)

.... 1. culpable

.... 2. platitude

.... 3. replete

.... 4. subjugate

.... 5. ostensible

.... 6. venerable

.... 7. salient

.... 8. scrupulous

a. to conquer

b. apparent

c. respected

d. conscientious

e. brief

f. blameworthy

g. commonplace remark

h. false

.... 9. transitory   i. filled up

.... 10. spurious   j. outstanding

REVIEW EXERCISE A Select from the following list the appropriate word for each space in the paragraph below and write it in the space. Use each word only once. (Add 5 points for each correct answer.)

antipathy	malicious	platitudes	subjugate
circumspect	ostensible	recalcitrant	transitory
culpable	ostracize	replete	unscrupulous
disparage	perfunctory	salient	venerable
malevolent	plagiarized	spurious	vindictive

I saw a confusing movie about the rivalry between two brothers who were both writers. Bret Brooks, the older, more established writer, was jealous of Bart, who, it was rumored, could write better. Up until recently, Bart had always taken guidance from Bret. However, literary circles had begun to (1) .... Bret's work and were circulating a story about Bret's (2) .... attempt to (3) .... Bart and force him to stay out of the limelight.

As the plot unfolded, Bret, feeling (4) .... toward his (5) .... brother, who was beginning to go out on his own, tried to (6) .... Bart from literary circles. The (7) .... cause of Bret's attempt was the younger brother's alleged effort to sell a short story which Bret claimed Bart had (8) .... from one of his unpublished manuscripts. This was a(n) (9) .... reason, however; the real reason was that Bret was jealous of his brother's blossoming literary success. Bart was beginning to be a(n) (10) .... figure among the younger writers of the city. He knew he was a better writer than Bret, whose trite work was (11) .... with (12) .... and tired plots, and whose stories were always written in a(n) (13) .... style as though they had been cranked out by a machine. The truth is that Bart, secure in the knowledge that he had himself written the story in question, knew he was not (14) .... in this matter, and, revealing a(n) (15) .... streak in his personality, adopted a(n) (16) .... attitude toward Bret. His revenge,

158   © 1977 HBJ

when it came, proved effective. Bret had been (17) ....
enough to steal from Bart's unpublished work. The revelation was a cruel
blow to the older brother's fans, who had long regarded their idol as the
most (18) .... of writers. His triumph having proved
(19) ...., Bret soon wished he had been more (20)
.... in handling the situation.

I hope I have gotten this straight. Who stole what from whom?

REVIEW EXERCISE B Follow the directions for the *Review Exercise* on page
87. Complete each of the following items with one of the words in parentheses. (Add
20 points for each correct answer.)

1. recalcitrant:obsequious::unscrupulous:....................
   (malicious, circumspect, peremptory, perfunctory)

2. nefarious:culpable::surfeited:...................
   (replete, exorbitant, venerable, salient)

3. pseudo:fallacious::enigmatic:...................
   (malevolent, cryptic, spurious, tacit)

4. malicious:vindictive::voracious:...................
   (impeccable, insatiable, ostensible, transitory)

5. ostensible:latent::officious:...................
   (intangible, inexorable, nefarious, diffident)

Using WHO and WHOM in Questions

The distinction between *who* and *whom* is ignored frequently in speaking and
generally in informal usage, but it is carefully observed in standard formal written
English. To determine which form you should use, follow the rules for pronoun usage:
who is in the nominative case and is used for subjects and predicate nominatives;
whom is in the objective case and is used for objects.

When *who* and *whom* are used to ask a question, they are interrogative pronouns.

EXAMPLES **Who** is your partner?   **Whom** did you see?

To determine whether to use *who* or *whom,* change the question into a statement,
even though this change may produce an absurd sentence.

Whom did you see?
You did see **whom**.   (*Whom* is now clearly the object of the verb *see.*)[1]

[1] In solving these *who-whom* problems, you may find it helpful to substitute *he-him* for *who-whom* respectively. *He* is
equivalent to *who,* and *him* is equivalent to *whom.* EXAMPLES: *Who* is your partner? Your partner is *he* (hence, *who*).
Whom did you see? You did see *him* (hence, *whom*).

Who is your partner?

Your partner is who. (*Who* is a predicate nominative after *is*, meaning the same thing as the subject *partner*.)

Who did you think it was?

You did think it was who. (Again *who* is a predicate nominative.)

Whom were you talking to?

You were talking to whom. (*Whom* is the object of the preposition *to*.)

Mistakes are seldom made when the interrogative form *who* is used as the subject of a verb.

EXAMPLES   Who did this?   Who made this pie?

EXERCISE   Whenever possible, rearrange each of the following uncompleted questions as a statement including *who* or *whom*. In the space at the left, write the letter that shows how the pronoun is used. Then write *who* or *whom* in the blank within the question in order to complete it correctly. (Add 10 points for each correctly marked sentence.)

a. subject of verb   c. object of verb
b. predicate nominative   d. object of preposition

.c.. A. *Whom* . do you want?

.... 1. .... were you with?

.... 2. .... did the voters elect?

.... 3. .... do you think she is?

.... 4. .... shall we call?

.... 5. .... wrote this story?

.... 6. .... did the judge exonerate?

.... 7. .... were you talking to?

.... 8. .... are you trying to convince?

.... 9. .... is our most venerable scholar?

.... 10. ...., in your opinion, is culpable?

REVIEW EXERCISE   In some of the following sentences the pronouns are correct; in others they are incorrect. In the space at the left, write the letter of the usage. If the pronoun is incorrect, draw a line through it and write the correct form above it. Remember to rearrange *who-whom* sentences when necessary. (Add 10 points for each correctly marked sentence.)

a. subject of verb   c. object of verb
b. predicate nominative   d. object of preposition

.d.. A. Sue was waiting for Joe and ~~he~~. *him*

.c.. B. Whom will José choose?

.... 1. Who did Mother mean?

.... 2. Rosa left us stragglers behind.

.... 3. Whom in this class has a bicycle?

.... 4. Malcolm and they preferred to stay home.

.... 5. The caller must have been she.

.... 6. Alicia and me were in a serious dilemma.

.... 7. Who does the doctor wish to speak with?

.... 8. It was them, Allen thought.

.... 9. Fran heard a malicious rumor about Larry and him.

.... 10. Whom is Deborah taking to the show?

Using WHO and WHOM in Subordinate Clauses

When *who* or *whom* introduces a subordinate clause, its case is governed by the same rules that you have learned for the personal and interrogative pronouns. *Who* is the nominative case form, used for subjects and predicate nominatives; *whom* is the objective case form, used for the object of a verb and the object of a preposition.

EXAMPLES   I remember who was there.   She is a woman whom I trust.

The case of the pronoun beginning a subordinate clause is determined by its use in the clause it begins. The case is not affected by any word outside the clause.

While you are learning to use *who* and *whom* correctly as relative pronouns, follow the three-step method listed below. Although the method is time-consuming at first, it will produce accurate results.

Step 1. Separate the clause from the rest of the sentence.

Step 2. Determine how the pronoun is used in the clause: subject of verb, predicate nominative, object of verb, or object of preposition.

Step 3. Select the correct form (*who* or *whom*) according to the case required by its use in the clause.

PROBLEM   He is a teacher (who, whom) everyone likes.

Step 1. (who, whom) everyone likes

Step 2. verb in clause = *likes;* subject of verb = *everyone;* object of verb = *who* or *whom?*

Step 3. Object of verb is in the objective case; hence the correct form is *whom.*

ANSWER   He is a teacher whom everyone likes.

PROBLEM   Do you know (who, whom) he is?

Step 1. (who, whom) he is [he is (who, whom)]

Step 2. verb in clause = *is;* subject of verb = *he;* predicate nominative = *who* or *whom?*

Step 3. Predicate nominative is in the nominative case; hence the correct form is *who.*

ANSWER   Do you know **who** he is?

Do not let parenthetical expressions like *I think, I believe,* and so on, mislead you. They are mere insertions and have no effect on the case of the pronoun.

PROBLEM   She is a girl (who, whom), I think, will succeed.

Step 1. (who, whom) will succeed

Step 2. verb in clause = *will succeed;* subject of verb = *who* or *whom?*

Step 3. Subject of verb is in the nominative case; hence the correct form is *who.*

ANSWER   She is a girl **who,** I think, will succeed.

EXERCISE   This exercise requires you to determine the correct form (*who* or *whom*) by following the three-step method described above. Fill in the lines below each sentence with the specified information. Then return to the sentence and draw a line through the incorrect form. Think! Do not guess! (Add 10 points for each correctly marked sentence.)

A. Everyone (who, ~~whom~~) uses an automobile owes a debt to Henry Ford.

  a. clause . . *(who, whom) uses an automobile* . . . .

  b. use in clause *subject of verb*   c. case and form *nominative-who*

1. Call Dr. Longstreet, (who, whom) the dentist recommended.

  a. clause . . . .

  b. use in clause . . . .   c. case and form . . . .

2. She did not tell me (who, whom) she was looking for.

  a. clause . . . .

  b. use in clause . . . .   c. case and form . . . .

3. We were seen by a man (who, whom), I was certain, would recognize us.

  a. clause . . . .

  b. use in clause . . . .   c. case and form . . . .

4. Do you know (who, whom) the umpire is?

  a. clause . . . .

  b. use in clause . . . .   c. case and form . . . .

5. She is one of the scientists (who, whom) I want to meet.

  a. clause . . . .

    b. use in clause. . . . .   c. case and form. . . . .

6. She is a girl (who, whom) I knew in summer camp.
    a. clause. . . . .

    b. use in clause. . . . .   c. case and form. . . . .

7. Have you heard (who, whom) the winners were?
    a. clause. . . . .

    b. use in clause. . . . .   c. case and form. . . . .

8. The case will be taken by (whoever, whomever) the court appoints.
    a. clause. . . . .

    b. use in clause. . . . .   c. case and form. . . . .

9. Do you know (who, whom), in the coach's opinion, would be the best captain?
    a. clause. . . . .

    b. use in clause. . . . .   c. case and form. . . . .

10. She is the gymnast with (who, whom) I am training.
    a. clause. . . . .

    b. use in clause. . . . .   c. case and form. . . . .

REVIEW EXERCISE In the space at the left, place the letter (*a, b, c,* or *d*) from the following list to show that you know how the pronoun is used. Draw a line through the incorrect pronoun. If you are in doubt, transpose the questions on a separate sheet of paper and, for relative pronouns, follow the three-step formula. A little time and thought will increase your accuracy. (Add 5 points for each correct sentence.)

> *a.* subject of verb   *c.* object of verb
> *b.* predicate nominative   *d.* object of preposition

. . . . 1. (Who, Whom) are you taking to the dance?

. . . . 2. That was probably (she, her).

. . . . 3. Should I believe you or (they, them)?

. . . . 4. She is a leader (who, whom) the people admire.

. . . . 5. He is one of the men (who, whom), I am sure, spoke to me.

. . . . 6. (Who, Whom) do you think it is?

. . . . 7. We talked with an old gentleman (who, whom), according to his story, had been a great hero.

. . . . 8. The blame fell on Betty and (me, I).

. . . . 9. I thought that you meant (we, us).

. . . . 10. (Who, Whom) shall we turn to for help?

. . . . 11. Did you ask both your father and (she, her)?

. . . . 12. Bonnie and (she, her) must make the decision.

. . . . 13. We will meet with the representatives (who, whom) the employees elect.

. . . . 14. It was (us, we) boys.

. . . . 15. Have you talked with Alex and (he, him)?

. . . . 16. He is a friend (who, whom) is always reliable.

. . . . 17. The driver and (I, me) were not injured.

. . . . 18. He asked (we, us) women for our opinion.

. . . . 19. (Who, Whom) did you think she was?

. . . . 20. Were these pictures drawn by Janet and (her, she)?

Using Pronouns in Incomplete Constructions

Study the following sentences. The words given in parentheses are normally and correctly omitted in writing or speaking. Observe that these incomplete constructions follow the words *than* or *as*.

1. Florence does better work than he (does).
2. My brother weighs more than I (weigh).
3. Are you as old as he (is)?
4. These boys are better dancers than they (are).

After than and as introducing an incomplete construction, use the form of the pronoun you would use if the construction were completed.

Sometimes the meaning of the sentence is revealed by the pronoun used.

I enjoyed the first speaker more than she (did).

I enjoyed the first speaker more than her (more than I enjoyed her).

EXERCISE Write in the space at the right of each sentence the part of the sentence beginning with *than* or *as*, using the correct pronoun and supplying the missing part of the sentence to show that the pronoun is correct. Then draw a line through the incorrect one of the pronouns in parentheses. (Add 10 points for each correct sentence.)

164

A. His sister learns more easily than (he, ~~him~~).   *than he does* . . . .

1. Jane is a better pianist than (she, her).   . . . .

2. Dorothy will leave later than (we, us).   . . . .

3. Senator Johnson did not speak as long as (he, him).   . . . .

4. I know Frances better than (she, her).   . . . .

5. We can do as well as (they, them).   . . . .

6. You are healthier than (I, me).   . . . .

7. Miss Hato gave me a better grade than (he, him).   . . . .

8. I can work faster than (she, her).   . . . .

9. You paid Terence more than (I, me).   . . . .

10. They don't study as hard as (we, us).   . . . .

REVIEW EXERCISE   If the pronouns in each of the following sentences are correct, place a + in the space at the right. If a pronoun is incorrect, draw a line through it and write the correct pronoun in the space at the right. (Add 4 points for each correctly marked sentence.)

1. Buy your tickets from Andrew or me.   1. . . . .

2. Julio is more dependable than him.   2. . . . .

3. Her and me took the early bus.   3. . . . .

4. Keep this a secret between you and I.   4. . . . .

5. Whom do you know in Detroit?   5. . . . .

6. He probably meant we seniors.   6. . . . .

7. The strange caller might have been him.   7. . . . .

8. I did not know who she was.   8. . . . .

9. She asked my father and I for help.   9. . . . .

10. Pete and her annoyed the teacher.   10. . . . .

11. Sam told him and I about his trip.   11. . . . .

12. Who were you talking about?   12. . . . .

13. Are you sure it was they?   13. . . . .

14. Mr. Clark took Phyllis and I to the exhibition.   14. . . . .

15. You are a better student than them.   15. . . . .

16. Give the message to Don and she.   16. . . . .

17. Who do you think will be appointed?   17. . . . .

18. Us girls offered to pay our own way.   18. . . . .

19. I thought that you and her were cousins.   19. . . . .

20. The store will hire whoever has the best credentials. 20. . . . .

21. Who are you waiting for?   21. . . . .

22. Charlotte usually does better than me in science. 22. . . . .

23. Don't expect them or us until tomorrow.   23. . . . .

24. Is Carol as tall as her?   24. . . . .

25. Who did he say he was?   25. . . . .

Chapter Review

EXERCISE In the space at the left, place the letter (*a, b, c,* or *d*) from the list below to indicate how the pronoun is used. Draw a line through the incorrect one of the two pronouns in parentheses. (Add 4 points for each correctly marked sentence.)

a. subject of verb	*c.* object of verb (direct or indirect)
b. predicate nominative	*d.* object of preposition

. . . . 1. Were you talking about the boys or (we, us)?

. . . . 2. I believe it was (they, them) who maligned us.

. . . . 3. I was a close friend of the young novelist, (who, whom) at that time was unknown.

. . . . 4. Judy and (I, me) are old friends.

. . . . 5. She accused both Armand and (I, me) of malicious intentions.

. . . . 6. Do you remember (who, whom) Jim said had won?

. . . . 7. Are you older than (she, her)?

. . . . 8. Your next co-worker will be either Ed or (she, her).

. . . . 9. I'll have to speak to Carlos and (he, him).

. . . . 10. I tried to get an interview with the editor (who, whom) the politicians disparage.

. . . . 11. You and (I, me) are in for trouble.

.... 12. Did you ask Dorothy and (she, her) where they had been?

.... 13. The Loyolas and (us, we) are spending the holiday together.

.... 14. Ostensibly, the reporters wanted to know (who, whom) the governor would appoint.

.... 15. You can play better than (I, me).

If a sentence is correct, place a + in the space at the right. If it is incorrect, cross out the pronoun and write the correct form in the space.

16. You can depend on Walter and I.   16. ....

17. We could not reach Helen and her.   17. ....

18. When you and them are ready, we'll go.   18. ....

19. He is the man who I met in Boston.   19. ....

20. His brother is twice as old as him.   20. ....

21. It could not have been she.   21. ....

22. Did you tell Sandra and she?   22. ....

23. I know of no one who at times is not discontented. 23. ....

24. Us freshmen didn't have a chance against the seniors. 24. ....

25. Have you heard from your father or her?   25. ....

LESSON 71

Cumulative Review

In most of the three-line sentences below, one line contains an error in punctuation or capitalization or usage or sentence structure. There is not more than one error in each sentence, and some sentences contain no errors. Write, in the space provided, the letter of the line in which the error appears. If there is no error, write a zero (0). (Add 5 points for each correct answer.)

1. A. Since you were unable to see   1. .....
   B. your assailant in the dark,
   C. how can you be sure it was him?
2. A. One out of every three homes that   2. .....
   B. hire a gardener have children
   C. able to do the gardener's work.
3. A. Rounding the corner of the   3. .....
   B. building to investigate the strange
   C. noise, my fears were confirmed.

4. A. Friendship is a basic need in
   B. everybody's life; without them we
   C. wouldn't be happy very long.

5. A. Hunting with my father will help me
   B. either to become a hunter or a trapper
   C. for the U.S. Forest Service.

6. A. Silas had returned to the farm
   B. because he wanted to be near the
   C. people he loved in his last moments.

7. A. A life membership in the association is
   B. handed to each president
   C. as they take office.

8. A. Everyone was wondering whom
   B. the new Prime Minister would appoint
   C. to fill the vacant office.

9. A. It was her who gave Macbeth
   B. the encouragement he needed when
   C. he was about to back down.

10. A. When purchasing a dress,
    B. the salesclerk made me angry
    C. by arguing about the size I needed.

11. A. Just because a school has a more famous
    B. name than other schools don't mean
    C. you will get a better education there.

12. A. I do not mean that those comic
    B. books should be eliminated
    C. that are really funny.

13. A. Mother thinks its foolish of us
    B. to start our cross-country trip with
    C. so little cash in our pockets.

14. A. What child will read a two-hundred-page
    B. novel when they can get the same story
    C. in a fifteen-page comic book?

15. A. I have never known a more sincere,
    B. conscientious, hardworking young woman
    C. than she.

16. A. Ms. Scotti, the principal, asked whether
    B. my Father was born in St. Louis, Missouri,
    C. or in St. Louis, Michigan.

17. A. On these roads the trip is much
    B. shorter than it used to be. Although
    C. the distance is the same.

4. .....

5. .....

6. .....

7. .....

8. .....

9. .....

10. .....

11. .....

12. .....

13. .....

14. .....

15. .....

16. .....

17. .....

18. A. "What's happened?" "Where have you been?"
    B. he asked, looking around in panic
    C. to see whether I was all right.

18. .....

19. A. After finding out that my plane
    B. would be two hours late,
    C. my frantic telephoning began.

19. .....

20. A. My uncle, who is always thinking of
    B. appearances, said he was revolted
    C. by my baggy sweater and dirty sneakers.

20. .....

Building Vocabulary

intrepid /in trép id/, *adj.* Fearless, brave, daring: *With our intrepid native guides showing the way, we came through the jungle unharmed.*

notorious /nō táur ē əs/, *adj.* Widely known but with a bad reputation. *Notorious* should be used to describe only a bad person. *Famous* is used to describe a person widely known for good deeds: *Many notorious outlaws appear in the history of the West.*

omniscient /om nísh ənt/, *adj.* Knowing everything; very wise. This word is derived from two Latin words: *omni* (all) + *scire* (to know) = *know all*. The word *omni* is a familiar prefix in English: *omnibus* = bus for all; *omnipotent* = all-powerful: *People who think themselves omniscient are often irritating to others.*

poignant /poín yənt/, *adj.* Painful; painfully moving or touching. *Poignant* is usually used to mean painful to the *feelings,* not to the physical senses. You would not say, for instance, that a soldier had suffered a poignant wound, but you might say you had read a *poignant* story, meaning, probably, that it had moved you deeply: *The poignant scene at the end left the audience wringing their handkerchiefs.*

reticent /rét ə sənt/, *adj.* Silent, reserved, not inclined to say much. The root of this word (*re + tacere*) is the same as that of *tacit* and *taciturn,* which, as you know, mean "silent": *Margaret would get better grades if she were not so reticent in class.*—**reticence**, *n.* *His reticence is the result of shyness.*

sardonic /sar dón ik/, *adj.* Bitterly scornful, sneering, sarcastic: *Nicholasa Mohr's sardonic humor angered many of her readers but delighted others.*

sinecure /sí na kyūr/, *n.* A position or office which requires little or no work, yet pays well; an easy job: *In this sleepy little village the position of constable is a sinecure.*

succinct /sək síngkt/, *adj.* Expressed briefly and clearly; concise: *When he returned, the scout gave a succinct report of his findings.*

truculent /trúk yə lənt/, *adj.* Fierce, cruel; showing a fierce manner; threatening: *When she is angry, she adopts a truculent attitude.*—**truculence**, *n.*

ubiquitous /y-ū bík wə təs/, *adj.* Being everywhere at the same time; present everywhere: *When you travel abroad, you find that Americans are the most ubiquitous people in the world.*

EXERCISE Draw a line through each italicized word or word group in the following sentences and write above it a word from this lesson which will give the same meaning. (Add 10 points for each correct answer.)

1. To members of the *widely and unfavorably known* gang, escape appeared impossible because the police were *everywhere at once.*

2. The little girl's simple tribute to the *brave and daring* man who had sacrificed his life for hers was, to us, most *painfully touching*.

3. When the colonel read the enemy commander's *concise* message, he gave a *bitterly scornful* grunt.

4. Perhaps if the teacher did not think of himself as *knowing everything*, his pupils would be less *silent and reserved* in challenging his statements.

5. Whenever anyone accused her of holding a *position which required no work*, she became *fierce and cruelly threatening*.

REVIEW EXERCISE Place in the space at the right the letter of the word which is closest in meaning to the italicized word. (Add 4 points for each correct answer.)

1. *coerced* by parents
   a. ostracized b. exonerated c. punished   d. forced   1. . . . .
2. his *adamant* position
   a. unyielding b. ambiguous c. favorable   d. enviable   2. . . . .
3. an obvious *charlatan*
   a. trick   b. advantage c. pretender   d. benefactor   3. . . . .
4. the *bigoted* politician
   a. well-fed   b. intolerant c. obsequious d. ostentatious 4. . . . .
5. *abstain from* drugs
   a. refrain   b. be ill from c. be revived d. be cured by   5. . . . .
      from   by
6. a *precarious* perch
   a. high   b. hazardous c. secure   d. unattainable 6. . . . .
7. surprisingly *amenable*
   a. feasible   b. capable   c. implacable   d. persuadable   7. . . . .
8. the *loquacious* child
   a. lively   b. talkative c. reticent   d. nearby   8. . . . .
9. done *with impunity*
   a. unwillingly b. in haste   c. without   d. without   9. . . . .
                                   penalty   result
10. an *enigmatic* answer
   a. expected   b. reasonable c. decisive   d. puzzling   10. . . . .
11. *chronic* illness
   a. constant   b. severe   c. mild   d. contagious   11. . . . .
12. *pertinent* comments
   a. fresh   b. appropriate c. critical   d. annoying   12. . . . .
13. an *incorrigible* nuisance
   a. not   b. uninten-   c. not serious d. great   13. . . . .
      correctable   tional

14. her *lugubrious* expression
    a. homely   b. sorrowful   c. worried   d. happy   14. ....
15. *immaculate* linen
    a. saintly   b. impervious   c. spotless   d. soiled   15. ....
16. *plausible* explanation
    a. reasonable   b. absurd   c. coherent   d. lucid   16. ....
17. my *beneficent* uncle
    a. opulent   b. crippled   c. malicious   d. kindly   17. ....
18. *pseudo*-leather
    a. durable   b. cheap   c. imitation   d. genuine   18. ....
19. *pernicious* rumors
    a. encouraging   b. facetious   c. incredible   d. hurtful   19. ....
20. *cursory* reading
    a. careful   b. superficial   c. interesting   d. scientific   20. ....
21. this *vindictive* response
    a. revengeful   b. helpful   c. expected   d. innocent   21. ....
22. *spurious* claims
    a. proven   b. justifiable   c. unreasonable   d. false   22. ....
23. an alarming *connotation*
    a. disagreement   b. opinion   c. implication   d. idea   23. ....
24. *assiduous* student
    a. foolish   b. lethargic   c. diffident   d. hard-working   24. ....
25. *replete with* errors
    a. marred by   b. full of   c. copied with   d. fearful of   25. ....

Spelling: Some Real Monsters

Our language contains certain words in which the sound-spelling relationship is unusually strained. The gulf between how these words sound and how they are spelled can be bridged only by a good memory. Generally, there are sound historical reasons for the unusually great discrepancy between how these words are pronounced and how they are spelled; but most of the time, the reasons do not help with the spelling.

Many such words can be put into categories. That is what has been done with the words in the lists below. In list *1* are words containing silent letters (printed in red). List *2* consists of words in which a letter or letters (printed in red) are pronounced in ways unusual in English. Pronunciations are given for some of these. List *3* contains words the pronunciations of which have become so condensed and slurred as to render practically no clue to their correct spelling. (The preferred pronunciation follows each word.)

You can learn to spell these words only by looking at them, writing them, and ultimately, by memorizing them. (You probably know the meaning of most of the words; if you are unsure of any, check their meaning in a dictionary.)

1	2	3	
chassis	boulevard	blackguard	/blág ərd/
exhilarate	brooch	boatswain	/bṓ sən/
gauge	camouflage	colonel	/kúr nə-l/
hearth	ennui /án wē/	forecastle	/fṓk sə-l/
hemorrhage	mauve /mōv/	gunwale	/gún ə-l/
hygiene	naive	lichen	/lī kə-n/
isthmus	recipe	tortoise	/táur təs/
kiln	sergeant	victual	/vít l/
pageant	sleuth		
pestle			
thyme			
vehement			
yacht			
zealot			

EXERCISE A   Choose any ten of the words in the three lists, and use each in a separate sentence that shows its meaning. (Add 10 points for each properly used word.)

1. ....

2. ....

3. ....

4. ....

5. ....

6. ....

7. ....

8. ....

9. ....

10. ....

EXERCISE B   Be prepared to write from dictation all of the words taught in this lesson.

EXERCISE C   With someone to record them on the board, make three class lists: the first consisting of five words with troublesome silent letters; the second, of five words with unusual or foreign letter sounds; the third, of five words containing

172

condensed or slurred letters. (Use words not taught in this lesson.) Copy the fifteen words in your notebook; study them, and be prepared to write them from dictation when they have been erased from the board.

1. .... 8. ....
2. .... 9. ....
3. .... 10. ....
4. .... 11. ....
5. .... 12. ....
6. .... 13. ....
7. .... 14. ....
15. ....

REVIEW EXERCISE Write from dictation each of the following words or names. (Add 10 points for each correctly spelled word.)

1. ensemble
2. concerto
3. cymbal
4. percussion
5. Schubert
6. xylophone
7. octave
8. Beethoven
9. saxophone
10. baritone

CHAPTER TEN

Using Verbs Correctly

Most problems in verb usage are derived from the fact that verbs change their form to indicate time. The past form of *swim*, for example, is *swam:* When the canoe overturned, we *swam* to shore. Yet you have undoubtedly heard people make the mistake of using *swum* as the past form: We *swum* to shore. Errors of this kind can be eliminated from your speech by the study and practice provided in this chapter. The other kind of verb error covered in the chapter is the use of the nonstandard verb form to indicate the time of an occurrence in relation to the time of another occurrence. You can remove these errors from your writing and speaking by learning the formation and uses of all the tenses.

LESSON 74

Principal Parts of Irregular Verbs

Verbs express present, past, and future time. The grammar term used to refer to the time of a verb is *tense*. A verb may express six tenses or times.

1. Present tense I walk.
2. Past tense I walked.
3. Future tense I shall walk.
4. Present perfect tense I have walked.
5. Past perfect tense I had walked.
6. Future perfect tense I shall have walked.

The basic forms of a verb are those from which the tense forms are made. There are four of these basic forms, which are called the *principal parts* of the verb.

1. Present   walk
2. Present participle (often walking
   used with a helping verb)[1]
3. Past   walked
4. Past participle (often   walked
   used with a helping verb)

Regular and Irregular Verbs *Regular* verbs form their past and past participle by adding *–d* or *–ed* to the present form of the verb.

PRESENT	PRESENT PARTICIPLE	PAST	PAST PARTICIPLE
pile	piling	piled	(have) piled
work	working	worked	(have) worked

[1] The various forms of *to be* (*am, is, are, was, were, have been*) and the forms of *to have* (*have, has, had*) are common helping verbs.

© 1977 HBJ

Irregular verbs do not form their past and past participle forms by adding *–d* or *–ed* to the present form of the verb. They form their past and past participle forms in other ways such as by a change in the vowel, by a change in consonants, or by no change at all.

PRESENT	PRESENT PARTICIPLE	PAST	PAST PARTICIPLE
see	seeing	saw	(have) seen
break	breaking	broke	(have) broken
hit	hitting	hit	(have) hit

Regular verbs, which always form their past and past participle forms in the simple way shown at the beginning of this lesson, present no usage problem. Irregular verbs, however, are the cause of a great many errors. In order to use irregular verbs according to standard usage, you must memorize their past and past participle forms so that you will be able to use them correctly.

The following list includes the irregular verbs which are most commonly misused. (The verbs *lie* and *lay* have been reserved for further treatment in Lesson 76.) Memorize the past and past participle forms of each verb so that you will use them automatically. Use the list for reference if necessary when you are working on the drills which follow. In memorizing the principal parts, repeat *have* with each past participle form to help you keep in mind the fact that this form is always used with a helping verb—*have, has, had, is, was, will be,* and so on. Say to yourself, *"beat, beat, have beaten; break, broke, have broken,"* etc. It is not necessary to memorize the present participle, since it is always formed in the same way—with an *–ing* ending. If you memorize the principal parts, you should make a perfect score on the exercises without referring to the list.

THIRTY-FIVE COMMON IRREGULAR VERBS

PRESENT	PAST	PAST PARTICIPLE	PRESENT	PAST	PAST PARTICIPLE
beat	beat	(have) beaten	ride	rode	(have) ridden
blow	blew	(have) blown	ring	rang	(have) rung
break	broke	(have) broken	rise	rose	(have) risen
burst	burst	(have) burst	run	ran	(have) run
choose	chose	(have) chosen	see	saw	(have) seen
come	came	(have) come	set (to put down)	set	(have) set
do	did	(have) done			
draw	drew	(have) drawn	sing	sang	(have) sung
drink	drank	(have) drunk	sit (to rest)	sat	(have) sat
drive	drove	(have) driven	speak	spoke	(have) spoken
fall	fell	(have) fallen	spring	sprang	(have) sprung
fly	flew	(have) flown	steal	stole	(have) stolen
freeze	froze	(have) frozen	swim	swam	(have) swum
give	gave	(have) given	swing	swung	(have) swung
go	went	(have) gone	take	took	(have) taken
grow	grew	(have) grown	tear	tore	(have) torn
know	knew	(have) known	throw	threw	(have) thrown
raise[1]	raised	(have) raised	write	wrote	(have) written

[1] Not an irregular verb but included here for use in exercises when the distinction between *rise* and *raise* is required. *Raise,* meaning "to force upward," may be followed by an object. *Rise* (to go up) is never followed by an object.

EXERCISE A As your teacher dictates the verbs in the left-hand column in the preceding lists, write in two columns the past and past participle forms of the dictated verbs.

If you have mastered the principal parts of these thirty-five irregular verbs, you should be able to make 100 per cent on the following exercise.

EXERCISE B Draw a line through the incorrect form of the verb in parentheses. (Add 2 points for each correct answer.)

1. I had always (gone, went) to school on the bus.
2. An hour later she (come, came) back.
3. A year ago she (gave, give) me her permission.
4. In yesterday's test I (did, done) every problem wrong.
5. All day smoke had been (rising, raising) from the forest.
6. One plane had (flew, flown) all the way above the clouds.
7. The dog was struck as it (run, ran) in front of a truck.
8. Have you ever (beat, beaten) Georgia in a tournament match?
9. No one (seen, saw) him leave when the police came.
10. You should have (rang, rung) the doorbell.
11. He would have won the race if he hadn't (fell, fallen) near the tape.
12. Leontyne Price has never (sang, sung) better than she did tonight.
13. Who was (sitting, setting) in my seat?
14. When the solution was stirred, the lighter liquid (rose, raised) to the surface.
15. The trainer thought Dean had (tore, torn) a ligament.
16. He had (threw, thrown) his money away on trifles.
17. When we (come, came) home, we found the doors locked.
18. N. Scott Momaday had (wrote, written) a novel before *The Way to Rainy Mountain* was published in 1967.
19. You should have (blown, blew) your horn if you wanted to pass.
20. The cat (sprung, sprang) to the window sill.
21. The rockets (rose, raised) several miles before losing power.
22. I had already (wrote, written) three letters to him.
23. You have (grown, grew) faster than your sister.
24. Gus had (rode, ridden) over on his new bicycle to see us.
25. They were (sitting, setting) in their right seats.
26. I wish I had (known, knew) he was coming.
27. The guests had (drunk, drank) all the punch.
28. Who (give, gave) you the money?
29. Had anyone (spoke, spoken) to Jaime?
30. We had (broke, broken) the key in the lock.
31. To (raise, rise) from a short runway, this plane needs rockets.
32. All we (saw, seen) at the fire was a crowd of people.
33. When the mains (burst, bursted), the street was flooded.

176

34. To preserve the fruit, we had (froze, frozen) it.
35. You should have (drew, drawn) a smaller picture.
36. Before dinner we (swam, swum) out to the raft.
37. All that night the lantern (swang, swung) in the wind.
38. Since the child had (ran, run) into the car, the driver was not to blame.
39. If he'd (gone, went) when we did, he'd have arrived on time.
40. I wish I had (took, taken) a course in typing.
41. Whatever he (did, done), I will forgive him.
42. We have (chose, chosen) our candidate.
43. If the money is gone, someone must have (stole, stolen) it.
44. Please come in and (set, sit) down for a minute.
45. I (seen, saw) this picture last year.
46. The doctor (did, done) all she could.
47. I could not have (drove, driven) this car any farther.
48. When I (come, came) for help, he refused me.
49. Prices are expected to (raise, rise) this fall.
50. We found him (sitting, setting) in the swing.

LESSON 75

Reviewing Irregular Verbs

EXERCISE A   In the space in each sentence, write the proper past or past participle form of the verb preceding the sentence. (Add 2½ points for each correct answer.)

rise   1. Yesterday the heavy fog .... before noon.

break   2. I thought you had .... your leg.

beat   3. We have been .... only twice.

choose   4. I had .... the wrong road.

come   5. We .... in after you did.

blow   6. The barn was .... down by a cyclone.

draw   7. She .... us a map of the shortest route.

burst   8. As we were turning a corner, the tire ....

fly   9. You could have .... here in two hours.

grow   10. That tree .... two inches last year.

know   11. You should have .... better.

give   12. I .... the letter to Gerard yesterday.

do   13. They .... the best they could.

write   14. I should have .... to you.

throw   15. Who .... these papers on the floor?

drink   16. Who .... the milk?

go   17. The boys had .... home.

ride   18. I've .... this horse many times.

run   19. We .... as fast as we could.

speak   20. The speaker should have .... more clearly.

steal   21. I was quite sure who had .... the pie.

swim   22. One of the girls had .... to shore for help.

take   23. I wish you had .... me along.

spring   24. Radishes .... up where we thought we had planted carrots.

drive   25. You must have .... very fast.

swing   26. In those days we .... across the brook on a long rope.

freeze   27. The river had .... solid.

ring   28. Someone had .... the fire bell.

tear   29. She had .... her stocking on a splinter.

sing   30. Aretha Franklin had .... in the choir for years.

see   31. I .... him just ten minutes ago.

fall   32. Fortunately the tree had .... away from the barn.

do   33. After school closed we .... our best to get jobs.

drink   34. In one minute he might have .... the poison.

sit   35. Somebody had .... on the cake.

ride   36. The team had .... all day in the bus.

run   37. When you called, I .... over to your apartment.

set   38. Entering the room, he .... the box on the table.

swim   39. Has anyone .... across the lake?

come   40. The accident happened just as we .... along.

EXERCISE B   Write a plus (+) before each correct sentence. Write a zero (0) before each incorrect sentence. If the sentence is incorrect, draw a line through the verb and write the correct form above it. (Add 5 points for each correctly marked sentence.)

                        © 1977 HBJ

.... 1. Has he did anything for which he may be culpable?

.... 2. Lola come in just as we were leaving.

.... 3. We set down at a table which was loaded with good food.

.... 4. This machine has already blown out three fuses.

.... 5. Ricardo, who is scrupulously honest, would not have stole the money.

.... 6. The village has growed much larger in recent years.

.... 7. Tons of rock had fallen into the gorge.

.... 8. X-rays showed that I had broken a bone in my foot.

.... 9. Who give you these disparaging criticisms?

.... 10. Kent swum the course in record time.

.... 11. Under the terrific pressure the old boiler had burst open.

.... 12. Rudolph has always obsequiously taken his brother's advice.

.... 13. You could easily have beat him by ten points.

.... 14. You might have chose a better place for a picnic.

.... 15. I wish you had spoken less peremptorily.

.... 16. The crowd raised their hero to their shoulders.

.... 17. Finally she come to believe in her own sagacity.

.... 18. Pam has rode on to Jean's house.

.... 19. No one could have thrown the ball that far.

.... 20. I seen you coming up the hill.

Using LIE and LAY Correctly

Many persons who rarely make mistakes in the use of other irregular verbs have trouble using *lie* and *lay* correctly. A few minutes of concentrated attention on these two verbs will clarify their use and remove any uncertainty.

First you must understand the difference in meaning between *lie* and *lay*. Then you must memorize the principal parts of each.

Lie means to rest, recline, be in a lying position. Lie never has an object.

PRINCIPAL PARTS   *lie, (is) lying, lay, (have) lain*

Lay means to put or place something. It may have an object.

PRINCIPAL PARTS   *lay, (is) laying, laid, (have) laid*

When you are learning to use these verbs, take your time in solving the problems. Follow this two-step formula:

1. Ask yourself whether the meaning of your sentence calls for the verb *lie* or the verb *lay,* that is, whether the meaning is "to rest" or "to put."

2. Ask yourself the *time* of the verb—present, past, future, and so on—and which of the principal parts expresses this time. When you have selected the correct one of the two verbs and have determined the time, or principal part, you can easily select the proper form.

PROBLEM	Yesterday I (lay, laid) down for a nap at two o'clock.
MEANING	recline—the verb then is *lie*
TENSE	past—the past form of *lie* is *lay*
SOLUTION	Yesterday I **lay** down for a nap at two o'clock.
PROBLEM	How long was he (lying, laying) there?
MEANING	recline—the verb then is *lie*
TENSE	present participle or *–ing* form, which is *lying*
SOLUTION	How long was he **lying** there?
PROBLEM	As soon as we reached the cabin, we (lay, laid) a fire in the fireplace.
MEANING	put or place—the verb then is *lay*
TENSE	past—the past form of *lay* is *laid*
SOLUTION	As soon as we reached the cabin, we **laid** a fire in the fireplace.

EXERCISE A   Write in the blanks below each sentence the meaning, the name of the principal part, and the correct one of the two verbs in parentheses. Also draw a line through the incorrect form. Refer to the following table of principal parts. (Add 10 points for each correctly marked sentence.)

	lie—to rest or recline	*lay*—to put or place
PRESENT	lie	lay
PRESENT PARTICIPLE	(is) lying	(is) laying
PAST	lay	laid
PAST PARTICIPLE	(have) lain	(have) laid

A. The troops were (~~laying~~, lying) in a vulnerable position.

a. meaning...... *recline* ..... c. correct form .... *lying* ......

b. prin. part..... *pres. part.* ...

1. Ominous clouds (lay, laid) along the horizon.

a. meaning.................. c. correct form ....

b. prin. part..................

2. He is notorious for his habit of (lying, laying) down on the job.

a. meaning.................. c. correct form ....

b. prin. part..................

180

3. I (lay, laid) the papers on your desk yesterday.

    a. meaning...................   c. correct form ....

    b. prin. part...................

4. Her diary, written in inscrutable shorthand, had (laid, lain) in the attic for a hundred years.

    a. meaning...................   c. correct form ....

    b. prin. part...................

5. Jerry could not remember where he had (lay, laid) the key.

    a. meaning...................   c. correct form ....

    b. prin. part...................

6. Polly (laid, lay) too long under the sun lamp.

    a. meaning...................   c. correct form ....

    b. prin. part...................

7. We found the boat (lying, laying) at anchor in a secluded cove.

    a. meaning...................   c. correct form ....

    b. prin. part...................

8. Apparently he had (laid, lain) there for several days.

    a. meaning...................   c. correct form ....

    b. prin. part...................

9. The dog is not allowed to (lie, lay) on the furniture.

    a. meaning...................   c. correct form ....

    b. prin. part...................

10. A small committee (laid, lay) down the rules for the rest of us to follow.

    a. meaning...................   c. correct form ....

    b. prin. part...................

EXERCISE B Write in the blank in each sentence the form of *lie* or *lay* which the sentence requires. Use the table of principal parts which follows, and take time to use the two-question formula. Do not guess. (Add 5 points for each correct answer.)

	lie—to rest or recline	*lay*—to put or place
PRESENT	lie	lay
PRESENT PARTICIPLE	(is) lying	(is) laying
PAST	lay	laid
PAST PARTICIPLE	(have) lain	(have) laid

1. If you .... down a while, you'll feel better.

2. Veronica must have .... her paintbox on my picture.

3. My parents don't want us to .... around the house all day.

4. Please .... your textbooks on the table.

5. .... on his back, he studied the clouds.

6. These trees have .... here since the hurricane.

7. Mute evidence of the storm's power .... all about us.

8. The county .... a new road here last year.

9. Two rattlers were .... asleep on a sunny ledge of rock.

10. Rugs which .... too long in the sun may fade.

11. Ed enjoys .... there and making sardonic remarks about us.

12. Take the packages and .... them down over there.

13. Two survivors were .... exhausted on a remote beach.

14. At a clandestine meeting, the crooks .... their plans.

15. .... a foundation below water level was a hard job.

16. We knew that the worst part of the trip .... behind us.

17. At 10:00 P.M. I .... my work aside and watched television.

18. Because her job is a sinecure, she can .... around all day.

19. .... flat and keep your head down.

20. Debris left by the flood is .... knee-deep on Main Street.

LESSON 77

Using Tenses Correctly

Consistency of Tense The tense form of a verb shows its time. Good writers are careful to use the tense which will express the time correctly. To express time correctly, a writer should be consistent in using verbs. If you begin a story or an article in the past tense, for instance, you should not shift to the present tense unless the time of the action shifts to the present.

NONSTANDARD The first day on the job Sam *came* to work on time, but the second and third days he *comes* in twenty minutes late. (Since the action of both verbs is past action, both verbs should be in the past tense. *Comes* should be changed to *came*.)

NONSTANDARD Joyce *looked* at the flat tire, *takes* off her coat, *rolls* up her sleeves, and *went* to work. [The shift from past tense (*looked*) to present tense (*takes, rolls*) and then back again to past tense (*went*) is meaningless because the entire action of the sentence took place in the past. *Takes* and *rolls* should be changed to *took* and *rolled*.]

Avoid unnecessary shifts in the tense of verbs.

NONSTANDARD   The senator *refused* to answer reporters' questions and the next day *criticizes* the press for leaping to conclusions.

STANDARD   The senator refused to answer reporters' questions and the next day criticized the press for leaping to conclusions.

Use the present tense to express a general truth, such as a scientific fact.

At first glance the verb in the present tense in each of the following sentences may seem to be inconsistent with the other verb in the sentence, but the present tense is used because it states something which is always true.

EXAMPLES   Captain Bartlett knew that in this latitude the Gulf Stream is (not *was*) twenty degrees warmer than the waters around it.

Dr. Bradley told me that in its early stages cancer is (not *was*) curable.

Terry did not know that Alaska is (not *was*) the largest state.

Use the past perfect tense (had) for the earlier of two past actions.

The tense form of a verb shows the time relationship between it and the other verbs in the sentence; that is, the tense form shows which of two actions came first, or whether the actions occurred at the same time.

In the first sentence in each of the following pairs, the verbs are incorrectly in the same tense, although the actions expressed obviously did not happen at the same time. In the second sentence in each pair, the verb expressing the earlier action has been correctly placed in the past perfect tense, which is formed with *had: had been, had gone,* and so on.

NONSTANDARD   On our return we *learned* that you *called.*
STANDARD   On our return we learned that you had called.

The past perfect (*had called*) is correct because it shows that the calling preceded the learning.

NONSTANDARD   Lois *was* able to win the race because she *trained* rigorously.
STANDARD   Lois was able to win the race because she had trained rigorously.

The past perfect (*had trained*) is correct; the training preceded the winning.

Use the past perfect instead of would have in if clauses expressing the earlier of two past actions.

NONSTANDARD   If you *would have* waited longer, we would have found you.
STANDARD   If you had waited longer, we would have found you.

NONSTANDARD	I'd have recited if Mr. Rowe *would have* called on me.
STANDARD	I'd have recited if Mr. Rowe <u>had</u> called on me.

EXERCISE A Study the tense of each verb in the following sentences. If the tenses are correct, make no changes. If the tenses are incorrect, cross out the incorrect verb and write the correct form above it. Some sentences may require more than one correction. (Add 5 points for each correctly marked sentence.)

A. Mother gazed angrily at the chaos which the boys ~~left~~ *had left* in the living room and ~~calls~~ *called* them back to restore order.

1. Miss Schultz said that Bastille Day, the French Independence Day, was celebrated annually on July 14.

2. If you left for the airport on time, you would have caught your plane.

3. In the twenties, America appeared to be traveling at breakneck speed along the beautiful road to prosperity, but the depression of 1929 abruptly wrecks the speeding juggernaut and very nearly damaged it irreparably.

4. Since we studied late the night before, we were sleepy the next day.

5. Dr. Brown said that both hot and cold applications are effective in treating a sprain.

6. If you would have asked me, I'd have given you permission.

7. The teacher wanted to know whether any bilingual students enrolled.

8. When Ms. La Peña had heard our reports, she asked me to write a succinct summary for the class.

9. A reticent public speaker, he would have resigned if I would have insisted on his making a speech.

10. The principal told us that character was more important than brains.

11. If you didn't encourage me, I would not have succeeded.

12. Although we were sure that someone broke into the house, we found upon investigation that nothing is stolen.

13. If Harvey Birch wanted to, he could have exposed General Washington for helping a prisoner to escape.

14. This farm was a beautiful estate, but by 1890 it was an overgrown and neglected ruin.

15. One of baseball's historic moments was the time in the 1932 World Series

when Babe Ruth impudently points to the spot in the bleachers where he was going to hit the ball and then hits it there.

16. Even our history teacher did not know that Accra was the capital of Ghana.

17. A real estate firm built a new housing development where the old tenements were.

18. If you would have told the truth, you'd have been better off.

19. If you did your work, you could have graduated from high school with your class.

20. Although she had intended to major in science, she changed her mind during her first year in college and became a mathematics major.

EXERCISE B   Draw a line through the incorrect verb forms in the following sentences and write the correct forms above them. A few sentences are correct. (Add 5 points for each correctly marked sentence.)

1. If he wouldn't have lied to me, I'd be willing to trust him.

2. Mrs. Tolles said yesterday that a cytoanalyzer was a device which speeds up the detection of cancer cells.

3. I finally answered her truculent letter, which had lain on my desk for several days.

4. Mona leaped from the lifeguard's bench, drags the lifesaving float to the water's edge, and dived with it through the heavy surf.

5. Development of an airliner which will rise vertically from an airport is one of the salient problems facing aircraft designers.

6. Although on first acquaintance I found him inscrutable, on closer association I came to understand him well.

7. Considering himself infallible, the mayor had peremptorily laid down a number of restrictions which displeased the public.

8. The other driver claimed that I ran him off the road, but he gave up his claim when the police show him our tire tracks.

9. If we wouldn't have brought the boats ashore, they would have been damaged.

10. As the cloud rose higher and higher, it assumes the shape of a gigantic mushroom.

11. Miss Farillo expressed the opinion that all French people loved to argue.

12. If you would have written to me, I could have helped you.

13. We saw the crash coming, but on the icy highway we were powerless to prevent it.

14. As a youth he had been an intrepid adventurer, but in his later years he was notorious for his unscrupulous use of his old friends.

15. The children had been warned many times of the dangers lying in wait for those who enter the swamp.

16. Ambrose Bierce said that a circus was a place where horses, ponies, and elephants were permitted to see men, women, and children acting the fool.

17. The football squad was in excellent physical condition because most of the boys were working as laborers during the summer.

18. His injuries would have been less serious if he would have lain still until the ambulance arrived.

19. The heavy rain which was falling all night ended during the morning, and the temperature, which was dropping since midnight, began to rise.

20. We thought it was a record of some kind when Janis got on base twice in the same game because she had been hit by a pitched ball.

Chapter Review

EXERCISE A   Make each sentence correct by drawing a line through the incorrect one of the two forms in parentheses. (Add 4 points for each correct answer.)

1. In the still air the cloud of black smoke (rose, raised) straight up.
2. By December the lake had (froze, frozen) over.
3. Who (drank, drunk) the last bottle of milk?
4. What she said is not as important as what she (did, done).
5. Father was waiting for me when I (came, come) home.
6. Ralph (ran, run) a better race than I.
7. Who (swam, swum) the channel this summer?
8. I had (wrote, written) those letters.

9. The doctor told me to (lie, lay) down.
10. Mrs. Goldman (rose, raised) rapidly to the top of her profession.
11. (Lying, Laying) too long in the hot sun is dangerous.
12. All day the wind (blowed, blew) from the south.
13. Roger Bannister (ran, run) the first four-minute mile.
14. I was embarrassed to find I had (fell, fallen) asleep in class.
15. Norma had (lain, laid) her racket next to mine.
16. I could not have (swam, swum) any farther.
17. We all (did, done) the best we could.
18. You left your glasses (lying, laying) on a chair.
19. Fortunately help (came, come) in time.
20. The new highway (lies, lays) parallel to the old one.
21. I didn't expect to be (beat, beaten) so badly.
22. You might have (chose, chosen) a better partner.
23. Have you ever (driven, drove) to Brookville?
24. The reasons he (gave, give) were ridiculous.
25. She hasn't (spoke, spoken) to me for days.

EXERCISE B Draw a line through the incorrect verb forms in the following sentences and write the correct form above them. Make no change in sentences that are correct. (Add 10 points for each correctly marked sentence.)

1. Ms. Block told us that today scientists and most people of the world used the metric system of measurement.

2. If the metric system was adopted by the United States in the nineteenth century, we would not have been measuring distance in feet and miles all these years.

3. It has been estimated that the United States loses between ten and twenty-five billion dollars a year because its measurements are not compatible with world standards.

4. The English system measures length in inches, feet, and miles; denotes weight in ounces and pounds; and gave volume in pints and quarts.

5. We were surprised to find out that the metric system measures in terms of meters and kilometers, grams and kilograms, and milliliters and liters.

6. If we would have understood that each unit of the metric system can be divided by ten, we would not have made mistakes.

7. By the end of the third lesson, we learned that one kilogram was composed of 1,000 grams and was equal to 2.2 pounds.

8. If we would have traveled twenty kilometers in a car, we would have covered 12.42 miles since one kilometer equals .621 miles.

9. After our journey we figured out that, according to the metric system, we traveled 80 kilometers.

10. When Congress received a study committee report on a changeover to the metric system, it votes in favor of the changeover.

Cumulative Review

If there is no error in a sentence, write *C* in the space at the right. If there is an error, cross it out and write the correct form in the space at the right. (Add 5 points for each correctly marked sentence.)

1. Few students are as recalcitrant as he.   1. . . . . . .

2. He is the man whom Don said would help us.   2. . . . . .

3. A friend always responds when you need them.   3. . . . . .

4. Either Sunny or Donna is going to drive.   4. . . . . .

5. A stranger snaps our picture as we walked along the street and tried to sell us the print.   5. . . . . .

6. A police car come along at just the right moment.   6. . . . . .

7. We found the map laying beneath the front seat of the car. 7. . . . . .

8. To observers, the rocket seemed to raise slowly.   8. . . . . .

9. Most of the politicians were not so sanguine about the election as the governor and she.   9. . . . . .

10. Every one of his comments were either truculent or sardonic. 10. . . . . .

11. She gave Delia and I some money to keep for her.   11. . . . . .

12. The outcome of the election would have been different if you would have helped us.   12. . . . . .

13. On the way home he found the wallet he lost on the way to school.   13. . . . . .

14. He was incredulous when we boys told him the truth.   14. . . . . .

15. The only choices we had were staying home and watching television or we could go to the movies.   15. .....

16. Each of the members are allowed to bring two guests.   16. .....

17. One of the planes are overdue.   17. .....

18. I was sitting between Mac and he.   18. .....

19. Was the gift intended for Melina or her?   19. .....

20. When a student wants to recite, they must stand up.   20. .....

DIRECTIONS   Read the paragraph below. Then answer the multiple-choice questions that follow by writing the letter of your choice in the space provided at the right. (Add 10 points for each correct answer.)

1 In gym class students learn good posture by doing various exercises, but bad posture is acquired during the rest of the day from the heavy loads of books cradled in their arms. **2** Walking from class to class, their loads of books pull them forward into a hunched-over posture. Which would horrify the gym teacher. **3** Every student who takes five academic subjects, has to carry at least five textbooks, a notebook, and one or two other volumes. The whole pile weighing something less than a ton. **4** The loads of books laying in their arms are bad enough, but us students also have to carry lunch and personal belongings. **5** Not only by the end of the day is a student exhausted but also warped into a permanent bend. **6** With tired arms and aching backs, the students face the unnerving experience of getting themselves and their portable libraries onto the bus or train. **7** Students have tried to solve the heavy baggage problem by carrying their books in sacks or briefcases, or they tie them with belts, or by buying or making huge shoulder bags. **8** After a painful journey from home to school a chorus of tired students asked their teacher why can't all our textbooks be paperbacks?

1 Which of the following revisions of the second part of sentence 1 is most nearly parallel in form with the first part?   1. . . . . .

 A . . . but they acquire bad posture from the heavy loads of books they cradle in their arms as they go about during the rest of the day.

 B . . . but as they go about with heavy loads of books cradled in their arms during the rest of the day, they acquire bad posture.

 C . . . but during the rest of the day they acquire bad posture by going about with heavy loads of books cradled in their arms.

2 Which of the following revisions expresses most clearly the idea in the first part of sentence 2?   2. . . . . .

 A Walking from class to class, a hunched-over posture is forced upon them by their loads of books.

 B Walking from class to class, they are pulled forward by their loads of books into a hunched-over posture.

 C They are pulled forward into a hunched-over posture by their loads of books, while walking from class to class.

190

3 Which of the following versions of the second part of sentence 2 is correct?

3. .....

   A . . . hunched-over posture. Which would horrify the gym teacher. (as in the passage)

   B . . . hunched-over posture which would horrify the gym teacher.

   C . . . hunched-over posture; which would horrify the gym teacher.

4 Which of the following revisions of sentence 3 is correctly punctuated?

4. .....

   A Every student who takes five academic subjects has to carry at least five textbooks, a notebook, and one or two other volumes. The whole pile weighing something less than a ton.

   B Every student, who takes five academic subjects, has to carry at least five textbooks, a notebook, and one or two other volumes, the whole pile weighing something less than a ton.

   C Every student who takes five academic subjects has to carry at least five textbooks, a notebook, and one or two other volumes, the whole pile weighing something less than a ton.

5 In which version of sentence 4 is the usage correct?

5. .....

   A The loads of books laying in their arms are bad enough, but we students also have to carry lunch and personal belongings.

   B The loads of books lying in their arms are bad enough, but us students also have to carry lunch and personal belongings.

   C The loads of books lying in their arms are bad enough, but we students also have to carry lunch and personal belongings.

6 In which revision of sentence 5 is the "not only . . . but also" construction most smoothly handled?

6. .....

   A By the end of the day, a student is not only exhausted but also warped into a permanent bend.

   B By the end of the day, not only a student is exhausted but also warped into a permanent bend.

   C Not only is a student exhausted by the end of the day but warped also into a permanent bend.

7 Which is the smoothest arrangement of sentence 6?

7. .....

   A With tired arms and aching backs, the students face the

191

unnerving experience of getting themselves and their portable libraries onto the bus or train. (as in the passage)

    B The students face the unnerving experience of getting themselves and their portable libraries onto the bus or train with tired arms and aching backs.

    C The students face the unnerving experience of getting themselves and their portable libraries with tired arms and aching backs onto the bus or train.

8 Which of the following revisions of sentence 7 most successfully corrects its faulty parallelism?   8. . . . . .

    A . . . the heavy baggage problem by carrying their books in sacks or briefcases, or tied them with belts, or bought or made huge shoulder bags.

    B . . . the heavy baggage problem by carrying their books in sacks or briefcases, tie them with belts, or buy or make huge shoulder bags.

    C . . . the heavy baggage problem by carrying their books in sacks or briefcases, by tying them with belts, or by buying or making huge shoulder bags.

9 Which of the following revisions of sentence 8 is correctly punctuated?   9. . . . . .

    A After . . . to school, a chorus of tired students asked their teacher "Why can't all our textbooks be paperbacks"?

    B After . . . to school a chorus of tired students asked their teacher, "Why can't all our textbooks be paperbacks."

    C After . . . to school, a chorus of tired students asked their teacher, "Why can't all our textbooks be paperbacks?"

10 If you had to remove one sentence from this passage, which of the following could be omitted without changing the basic meaning of the passage?   10. . . . . .

    A sentence 2

    B sentence 3

    C sentence 6

LESSON 80

Building Vocabulary

chaos /kǎ os/, n. Confusion, complete disorder. The imagined state of the universe before any system or order was brought about is referred to as *chaos;* hence the word has come to be applied to any state of affairs which is lacking in orderliness:

Chaos followed the explosion in the school laboratory.—chaotic /kā ót ik/, *adj. After the party the room was in a chaotic condition.*

clandestine /klan dés tin/, *adj.* Done with secrecy, usually for an evil purpose; underhanded: *The uprising was carefully planned during a clandestine meeting of the chief rebels.*—**clandestinely** /klan dés tin lē/, *adv.*

extant /ék stənt/, *adj.* Still in existence: *Not all of Shakespeare's work is extant.*

gullible /gúl ə bə-l/, *adj.* Easily deceived or cheated: *An ingenuous person is likely to be gullible. Because she is so gullible, she is often the object of her friends' jokes.*

inscrutable /in skrū́ tə bə-l/, *adj.* Not understandable. A thing is *inscrutable* when it is so mysterious that you cannot figure out its meaning: *His expressionless face made him inscrutable.*

ludicrous /lū́ də krəs/, *adj.* Laughable; amusingly absurd: *A stage fight or duel must be carefully rehearsed so that it will not be ludicrous.*

ominous /óm ə nəs/, *adj.* Threatening; foreshadowing something bad. An *omen* is a sign indicating something in the future. An omen may be good or bad. A black cat is considered a bad omen. The word *ominous,* which is related to *omen,* is usually used to mean that something bad may happen: *We heard an ominous roll of thunder. The motor was making ominous sounds.*

sacrilegious /sák rə líj əs/, *adj.* Injurious to or disrespectful of sacred things or persons. Note carefully the spelling of this word, which is derived from two Latin words: *sacer,* meaning "sacred," and *legere,* meaning "to pick up." Originally *sacrilege* meant "stealing sacred things." *Sacrilege* now has a broader meaning on which the word *sacrilegious* is based: *The motion picture, which seemed to poke fun at the Church, was condemned as sacrilegious.*

vacillate /vás ə lāt/, *v.* To waver; to change one's mind back and forth: *Facing this serious emergency, I knew I must not vacillate.*—**vacillation,** *n.* *Leaders must make decisions quickly; they have no time for vacillation.*

vulnerable /vúl nər ə bə-l/, *adj.* Capable of being injured; open to attack: *Cut off from supplies and out of ammunition, the troops were vulnerable.*

EXERCISE In each space in the right-hand column, write a synonym or brief definition of the italicized word in the line at the left. (Add 10 points for each correct answer.)

1. Since the message was *inscrutable,* we did not know
   how *ominous* it was.   . . . .

   . . . .

2. When the politicians' *clandestine* agreement with   . . . .
   the underworld was revealed, their party was extremely *vulnerable.*

   . . . .

3. Thinking I was *gullible,* the bookseller told me he   . . . .
   had the only *extant* copy of the book.

   . . . .

4. It is *ludicrous* to accuse the Reverend Thomas White   . . . .
   of preaching a sermon which was *sacrilegious.*

   . . . .

5. Our leader *vacillated* so long before making his de-   . . . .
   cision that the entire organization was reduced to
   a *chaotic* state.

   . . . .

REVIEW EXERCISE A Distinguish between the words in each of the following pairs by writing after each a synonym or brief definition. (Add 10 points for each correct answer.)

1. incredible ....; incredulous ....
2. ostentatious ....; ostensible ....
3. homogeneous ....; heterogeneous ....
4. ingenious ....; ingenuous ....
5. venerable ....; vulnerable ....

REVIEW EXERCISE B In the blank at the right of each line, write a synonym or a brief definition of the italicized word. (Add 5 points for each correct answer.)

1. *impeccable* behavior ....
2. *succinct* report ....
3. *cryptic* answer ....
4. *ubiquitous* alumni ....
5. *malevolent* relatives ....
6. *truculent* opposition ....
7. *transitory* happiness ....
8. *plebeian* taste ....
9. *culpable* neglect ....
10. boring *platitudes* ....
11. a shameful *sinecure* ....
12. an *unscrupulous* deed ....
13. a *mundane* affair ....
14. *sardonic* humor ....
15. a *taciturn* man ....
16. an *intrepid* lifeguard ....
17. a *nefarious* plan ....
18. *coherent* writing ....
19. *notorious* criminal ....
20. *inexorable* determination ....

Spelling: Troublesome Literary Words

Many of the terms you encounter in your study of literature have unexpected and troublesome spellings. Unlike most common spelling demons (which are constantly taught and retaught), you probably neither see nor hear these literary terms often enough to remember them when you need to write them. (The terms presented in this lesson apply not only to literature, but often to movies and television programs as well.)

The spelling problems involved have been grouped into "categories." It may help you to learn them in these groups.

● TROUBLESOME *e*

allegory	A form (usually long) in which abstract qualities (goodness, truth, virtue) are represented by concrete characters, with the purpose of teaching a moral.
comedy	A form of drama which aims mainly to amuse and uplift and which has a happy ending.
elegy	A lyric poem expressing sorrow or thoughtfulness on themes of loss and death.
hyperbole	A deliberate exaggeration for the purpose of emphasis or humor.
imagery	The use of vivid descriptions of sense experience.
simile	Comparison of two apparently different things by using the word *like* or *as* or *so*.
tragedy	A drama of serious nature ending in misfortune for the protagonist. (See *protagonist* below.)

● TROUBLESOME *o*

irony	A figure of speech (humorous or sarcastic) in which what is said by the speaker or writer is really the opposite of what is meant.
melodrama	A romantic and sensational form of drama that depends upon suspense, exaggerated emotions, etc., for its appeal.
parody	An intentionally ridiculous imitation of a literary work or style.
protagonist	The chief character in a poem, story, play, or novel.
symbol	Something concrete that is chosen to represent something else, usually an abstract idea or quality. (The eagle is the symbol of the United States.)

● TROUBLESOME *a*

ballad	A narrative song or poem, usually of popular origin, and usually having a refrain.
metaphor	A figurative expression in which one thing is likened to another by speaking of it as if it *were* that other. (She is a regular magpie.)
parable	A short narrative that conveys some moral or truth by comparison with natural or common things.
pentameter	A line of poetry containing five accents or feet.

- DOUBLE LETTERS

a**ll**iteration — The repetition of the same sound (usually a consonant) at the beginning of two or more consecutive words.

a**ss**onance — The repetition of the same or similar vowel sounds in syllables that have different consonants.

so**nn**et — A complete poem of fourteen lines in iambic pentameter. (See *iambic* below.)

- TRICKY ENDINGS

burles**que** — A composition that provokes laughter by ludicrous imitation or satire of a subject—usually a serious or dignified one.

epi**c** — A long narrative poem, written in an elevated style, dealing with the deeds of a national or mythical hero.

iambi**c** — Consisting of or characterized by the use of *iambs*. (An *iamb* is a poetic foot consisting of an unstressed syllable followed by a stressed syllable.)

lyri**c** — Referring to poetry that is personal, musical, and emotional.

limeri**ck** — A humorous verse of five lines in which the first, second, and fifth lines have three accents and rhyme with each other; and the third and fourth have two accents and rhyme with one another.

- SILENT *ue*

dialog**ue** — A literary work in which two or more persons are represented as conversing.

epilog**ue** — A short, concluding section added to a literary work which summarizes, completes, amplifies, or comments on the work.

monolog**ue** — A play or dramatic composition for one actor only.

prolog**ue** — A spoken introduction (often in verse) to a poem or play.

- MISCELLANEOUS PROBLEMS

on**o**mat**o**p**oeia** — The use of words whose sound suggests the object or action that produces the sound (*crackle, quack,* etc.).

solil**o**quy — A speech made by a character alone or apart from others on the stage.

EXERCISE A   Be prepared to write from dictation all of the words taught in this lesson.

EXERCISE B   Choose ten of the terms taught in this lesson and use each in a separate sentence that indicates understanding of the term. (Add 10 points for each properly used word.)

1. ....

2. ....

3. ....

4. ....

5. ....

196

6. ....

7. ....

8. ....

9. ....

10. ....

EXERCISE C As your teacher writes them on the board, make a class list of ten literary terms (other than those taught in this lesson) that have caused spelling problems. Copy the terms in a notebook. They will then be erased. Now study them, and be prepared to write them from dictation. (Add 10 points for each correctly spelled word.)

1. .... 6. ....

2. .... 7. ....

3. .... 8. ....

4. .... 9. ....

5. .... 10. ....

REVIEW EXERCISE The phonetic spellings of five difficult words are given below. Using the charts on pages 248 and 249 (if you need to), say each word softly to yourself. Then write the correct nonphonetic spelling in the blank. (Add 20 points for each correctly spelled word.)

1. /gún ə-l/ .... 4. /lí kə-n/ ....

2. /án wē/ .... 5. /blág ərd/ ....

3. /bṓ sən/ ....

Part Four
WRITING COMPOSITIONS

Everything you have learned in your study of Parts One, Two, and Three of this workbook should be applied in the writing assignments in Part Four. Parts One to Three concentrate on the details of good writing: correct grammar and usage, accurate mechanics, and effective sentence structure. Part Four concentrates on broader matters of style, organization, and content.

The composition assignments in Part Four will give you practice in two kinds of writing: informal and formal. Since informal writing is more natural and therefore easier, the assignments in informal writing precede those in formal writing. The writing skills taught in the first three lessons will help you to write interestingly. These lessons review ways to make your style vivid and colorful. The skills taught in the rest of the lessons will help you to write clearly and convincingly. These lessons review paragraph structure, outlining and organization, and such practical kinds of formal writing as the business letter and the research paper.

Steps in Planning and Writing You will always write better compositions if you follow these six steps:

1. List your ideas.
2. Organize your ideas in a brief outline.
3. Write a first draft.
4. Proofread and revise.
5. Write the final draft.
6. Proofread again.

Proofreading is the process of finding and correcting errors. Since your composition should be as free from mechanical errors as possible, you must develop the habit of proofreading carefully everything you write.

Revising is a more positive process than the error-hunting of proofreading. It involves changes in vocabulary, in sentence structure, and in organization to make your writing clear, effective, and interesting.

Unless you are writing under time pressure, as in an examination, you should write two drafts. Never be satisfied with your first draft. The second draft will always be better.

Description in the Personal Narrative

All writing contains description, but *narrative* writing relies on it most heavily. The barest account of a personal experience is a narrative, but to be a good narrative, the account must describe in detail and with vigor and originality the people, scenes, and events of the story. Your first writing assignment will be to make a personal narrative interesting by means of vivid description.

You might ask, "What is vivid description?" First, description is vivid if the reader is affected by it. Second, description is vivid if the writer has chosen just the right words to express precise feelings, possibly discarding one word after the other until a satisfactory word is found. Adjectives, which are the obvious descriptive words, must be carefully chosen; but the good descriptive writer selects nouns, verbs, and adverbs with equal care. Always try for the best word. Remember what Mark Twain said: "The difference between the right word and the almost right word is the difference between lightning and the lightning bug."

EXERCISE A The writer of the following description chose his words carefully. Read the passage and draw a line under words which you think make the description effective. Note that while the passage is a narrative of a personal experience—a mountain climbing expedition—it is almost wholly dependent upon description for its success.

The hateful scree was below us. We were on blessed solid rock. For all of ten steps, that is. Then we came off the rock onto snow. The snow was soft and crustless in the midday sunshine, and we sank in to the knee, the thigh, the waist. I lurched. I floundered. In no time my mouth was open like a bloated fish's, gasping for air, and my heart was pounding fit to crack my ribs.

Even Thomas was not quite superhuman. He sank in too. But sinking or not, he was able to keep going steadily, whereas my ratio of movement to rest was about one to three. On the downslopes of the ragged rim my gait was a stumbling crawl. On the upgrades, which of course predominated, the crawl seemed in comparison to have been a light-footed sprint.

We searched for snowless rock. But now there was snow everywhere. Ahead, on the endless hummocks of the rim; to the right, choking the crater; to the left, falling away endlessly in billowing waves of glacier. The snow gleamed. The snow glared. The billows were no longer static but undulating, and from their crests darted long white lances of light that struck blindingly into my eyes. I fumbled in a pocket for my goggles but didn't find them. I had them on. The whiteness beat against their green lenses as if it would crack them with its force.

In that frozen world it was not cold. It was warm, even hot. Sweat was trickling on my back and down my forehead, under the goggles, into my eyes. My eyes were bothering me even more now than legs, lungs, or heart. Sweat and snow seemed to mingle, forming patterns and images that wove before me. Soon the whole mountaintop was weaving. Crater and rim revolved slowly in space, like an enormous wheel.

I was terribly tired, and the snow was soft. It was a great pillow, a featherbed, all around me, and in the deep drifts, leaning against it, I closed my eyes. I had read, sometimes even written, of climbers overwhelmed by sleep at high altitudes, and now for the first time it was actually happening to me. With eyes closed, the awful glare was gone. Resting motionless in my featherbed, I felt breathing and heartbeat ease, and I sank gently, deliciously, into a shadowed doze. Luckily the shadows never closed in entirely. My head jerked back. My eyes opened. I crept on again, willing myself to move, my eyes to stay open.[1]

—JAMES RAMSEY ULLMAN

EXERCISE B Listed below are ten common sights. After reading the list, select five which you would enjoy describing. On a sheet of paper, write a descriptive sentence for each of the five. Show that through careful selection of words, you can make a common experience interesting by describing it in an uncommon way. Your teacher may ask you to underline the descriptive words that you consider most effective.

A. A plane crossing blue sky: *Flashing silver against a blue backdrop, a plane arrowed steadily toward the horizon.*

1. Sunlight on water
2. A three-year-old girl running to greet her mother
3. A high school student climbing onto a bus in the morning
4. A quarterback executing a successful forward pass
5. A ball player hitting a home run
6. Your brother or sister packing the trunk of the car
7. The atmosphere after a thunderstorm
8. A beginning driver making a left turn
9. The view from a familiar hilltop
10. A teacher in front of the class

WRITING ASSIGNMENT Select from your experience, preferably your recent experience, an incident which made an impression on you. In 150–200 words, tell what happened, making your account interesting through careful selection of vivid words. Underline, as your teacher directs, the words and phrases you are especially proud of. You need not burden your account with an unnatural number of descriptive words, but you should have at least five good ones.

[1]From "Kilimanjaro!" by James Ramsey Ullman. Copyright 1958 by James Ramsey Ullman. Reprinted by permission of Harold Matson Company, Inc.

Description: Sense Words

In your first writing assignment you described an incident from your experience, concentrating on careful selection of descriptive words. In this lesson you will take the next step, concentrating on words which appeal to the senses, especially the senses of touch, smell, and hearing, which are less commonly employed in description than the sense of sight. Undoubtedly you used some sense-appeal words in your first assignment, but perhaps you did not do so deliberately. In this lesson, you should make a deliberate attempt to strengthen your descriptive writing by means of sense-appeal words.

Read the following descriptive passages, which are effective because they appeal to the reader's senses. Identify the senses to which each passage appeals.

1. Fighting sleep now, driving more slowly, he felt the road swing left and dip into the canyon. . . . Where the State highway turned left, he drove straight ahead and followed the narrower and bumpier road along the South Fork—his own river. Close to the water, with the down-canyon wind moving, the air was cooler than it had been on the ridge. The engine seemed to purr more smoothly, even though the road ran up-grade steadily. Below the road, to the right, he heard the deep murmur of the stream, and saw a vague whiteness as the water came down a chute between rocks.[1]

2. To the men on the line the fire was red glare in the eyes and reaching flame, roar and crackle in the ears, choking in the throat, fierce heat on the face. The fire possessed them and beat in upon their senses.[1]

3. At the ridge top he reined in the little black mare and listened and looked. . . . Sounds poured in upon him. Close at hand he heard the *click-clank* of handtools rasping at the earth and knocking on stones. There was the slow *clunk . . . clunk . . . clunk* of an ax. Farther off he distinguished the rumbling of a truck and the angry roaring of a cat. Suddenly the staccato of a power-saw burst out, stuttered for a moment, and then took hold with a crescendo.[1]

4. Under the wuthering arch of the high wind a V of wild geese fled south. The rush of their pinions sounded briefly, and the faint, plaintive notes of their expeditionary talk. Then they left a still greater vacancy. There was the smell and expectation of snow, as there is likely to be when the wild geese fly south. From the remote distance, toward the red sky, came faintly the protracted howl and quick yap-yap of a prairie wolf.[2]

5. In the porch where Ursula sat there was a great noise of girls, who were tearing off their coats and hats and hanging them on racks bristling with pegs. There was a smell of wet clothing, a tossing out of wet, draggled hair, a noise of voices and feet.[3]

[1] From *Fire* by George R. Stewart. Copyright 1948, by George R. Stewart. Reprinted by permission of the author.
[2] Excerpt from "The Portable Phonograph," by Walter Van Tilburg Clark. Copyright 1941, © 1969 by Walter Van Tilburg Clark from *The Watchful Gods and Other Stories,* by Walter Van Tilburg Clark. Reprinted by permission of International Creative Management.
[3] From *The Rainbow* by D. H. Lawrence.

EXERCISE Select three of the following subjects and write a three- or four-sentence description of each, using words and phrases which appeal to the senses. Ask yourself what sights, sounds, smells, feelings, or tastes are present in the experience. Then try to find original ways of describing them.

1. A hot night in the city
2. Riding a ten-speed bike
3. The interior of a store
4. Driving a tractor on a hot, dusty day
5. The kitchen just before dinner
6. A garage or machine shop
7. The woods at night
8. Taking off in a plane
9. Inside the school bus
10. Making a high dive

WRITING ASSIGNMENT Write a personal narrative (200–300 words) in which you make the experience real to the reader by means of words that appeal to the senses. It is, of course, easy to overdo sense appeals by trying too hard to get all five senses into a short description. Even if the writing should seem strained, the effort is worthwhile as training.

You may wish to choose a topic from the following list:

A visit to a carnival, amusement park, zoo, or circus
A motorcycle ride
Playing in a close game
A picnic, a family reunion, or a party
Last period study hall on a hot day
An overnight camping experience or a canoe trip
A school dance
A hurricane, blizzard, or other storm
The first day on a summer job
A rescue

LESSON 84

Description: Figurative Language

A third way of making writing interesting and lively is through the use of figures of speech, or figurative language. When writers express ideas figuratively, they are thinking in comparisons. They say or imply that one thing is like another, and in so doing make descriptions more vivid and more meaningful. The things compared in a figure of speech are not actually alike, but the writer sees at least one way in which they resemble each other. Comparing a man's chin to a peninsula, for example, makes clear what the chin is like, even though there is really very little similarity between a chin and a peninsula.

Read the following example of figurative writing:

The conductor scraped with his foot and flapped his arms like a rooster about to crow, and the bandsmen sitting in the green rotunda blew out their cheeks and glared at the music. Now there came a little "flutey" bit—very pretty!—a little chain of bright drops.[1]

—KATHERINE MANSFIELD

[1] From "Miss Brill" from *The Garden Party* by Katherine Mansfield.

Two ways of expressing a comparison are shown in this example—two kinds of figures of speech. The first is called a *simile*. When the writer says that the band conductor "flapped his arms like a rooster about to crow," she achieves her comparison in an obvious way—by using the comparing word *like*. A simile is a comparison which uses a comparing word—*like* or *as*.

The second figure of speech in the selection above is called a *metaphor*. When writers imply or suggest comparisons but do not use comparing words, they create metaphors. Here, when Katherine Mansfield refers to the notes of the flute as a "chain of bright drops," she is comparing notes to drops of water and the succession of notes to a chain. This figure of speech is a metaphor because in it a comparison is made without a comparing word.

Figures of speech may be brief, requiring only one or two words: *cavernous* mouth, *network* of streets, *leathery* face, *dancing* leaves, in the *teeth* of the wind. Many figures of speech have become so ordinary that they have lost their effectiveness: busy *as a bee,* clear *as crystal,* white *as a sheet.* Such commonplace figures should be avoided.

The power of a figure of speech lies in its originality and its aptness. You usually react to an effective figure of speech with the feeling that the writer has spoken the truth. The kind of clarity that has been expressed makes you say to yourself, "Good! That's just the way it is!"

EXERCISE Underline the words that make comparisons in the following sentences, as in the examples on this page. Be prepared to discuss with your classmates the merits of each comparison.

1. A seat in this boat was not unlike a seat on a bucking broncho. The craft pranced and reared, and plunged like an animal. —STEPHEN CRANE

2. Authority without wisdom is like a heavy axe without an edge, fitter to bruise than polish. —ANNE BRADSTREET

3. He watched the ground frost heave up icy fingers. —JAMES BOYD

4. They stared at the rhinoceros . . . his hide covered with rusty patches like the joints of ancient armor. —JOSEPHINE JOHNSON

5. His face was shrouded in a thousand veils of caution. —JAMES BOYD

6. The name "New York" glittered in front of her like the silver in the shops on Michigan Boulevard. —GWENDOLYN BROOKS

7. silent as a held breath —JAMES AGEE

8. In two days it blew a gale. The *Judea,* hove to, wallowed on the Atlantic like an old candle-box. It blew day after day; it blew with spite, without interval, without mercy, without rest. The world was nothing but an immensity of great foaming waves rushing at us, under a sky low enough to touch with the hand and dirty like a smoked ceiling.
   —JOSEPH CONRAD

9. She carried a thin, small cane made from an umbrella, and with this she kept tapping the frozen earth in front of her. This made a grave and persistent noise in the still air, that seemed meditative like the chirping of a solitary little bird. —EUDORA WELTY

10. Persons with any weight of character carry, like planets, their atmospheres along with them in their orbits. —THOMAS HARDY

WRITING ASSIGNMENT This third writing assignment, like the first two, is to be an account of a personal experience, in from 200 to 300 words. It should be made interesting by skillful description. The description, while accomplished by means of carefully selected descriptive words and words which appeal to the senses, should also include some effective figurative language. As you describe objects and actions, think in terms of likenesses. Ask yourself, "What was it like? What did the person look like?" When you have written your composition, underline the figures of speech.

If you need suggestions, the following may be helpful:

A moonlight swim
Falling in love for the first time
An experience which taught you a lesson
A deed I am ashamed of
My proudest moment
An act of heroism
A wrong decision
A family disagreement
A fascinating personality
Roughing it
A block party
A day to remember
A subway ride
A dangerous encounter
My first game of bowling (tennis, golf, football, etc.)

LESSON 85

Paragraph Structure

The three Writing Assignments you have done called for informal writing. The remaining Writing Assignments require formal writing. Much that you learned about description will be applicable in these assignments, but formal writing requires tighter organization and a more serious attitude toward your subject.

Beginning with the topic sentence, Lessons 85, 86, and 87 review the structure of a paragraph, a subject with which you are undoubtedly familiar.

THE TOPIC SENTENCE

A well-organized paragraph develops in a logical manner the meaning of one sentence in the paragraph. This sentence is the <u>topic sentence</u>.

In most one-paragraph compositions the topic sentence is the first sentence. Placed in this position, it announces the subject to be discussed; the readers know immediately what the paragraph is to be about. In some paragraphs the topic sentence also states the writers' attitudes toward their subjects—how they feel about them. The readers know as they begin to read the paragraphs that they will find the proof or the reasons which support the writers' attitudes.

Read the following model paragraphs. Notice that in paragraph 1 the writer announces the topic in the opening sentence—the physical characteristics of an ocean wave. The entire paragraph is devoted to describing these characteristics.

Paragraph 2 begins by referring to the mistake of selecting a vocation simply because you know somebody who is successful in that vocation. The paragraph gives the writer's reasons for considering this a mistake.

1. Before constructing an imaginary life history of a typical wave, we need to become familiar with some of its physical characteristics. A wave has height, from trough to crest. It has length, the distance from its crest to that of the following wave. The period of the wave refers to the time required for succeeding crests to pass a fixed point. None of these dimensions is static; all change, but bear definite relations to the wind, the depth of the water, and many other matters. Furthermore, the water that composes a wave does not advance with it across the sea; each water particle describes a circular or elliptical orbit with the passage of the wave form, but returns very nearly to its original position. And it is fortunate that this is so, for if the huge masses of water that comprise a wave actually moved across the sea, navigation would be impossible. Those who deal professionally in the lore of waves make frequent use of a picturesque expression—the "length of fetch." The "fetch" is the distance that the waves have run, under the drive of a wind blowing in a constant direction, without obstruction. The greater the fetch, the higher the waves. Really large waves cannot be generated within the confined space of a bay or a small sea. A fetch of perhaps 600 to 800 miles, with winds of gale velocity, is required to get up the largest ocean waves.[1]

—RACHEL CARSON

2. Sometimes young people make the mistake of picking a job just because a much admired relative or friend likes that job. If your favorite uncle is a plumber, maybe you will make a good plumber too—but not necessarily. It is risky to choose an occupation just because you admire or are fond of someone who has chosen it. You may admire Joe Namath, or Representative Shirley Chisholm, or the corner druggist, or the man who runs the "fixit" shop. But this does not mean that you can count on being successful or happy as a professional football player, or in a high post in government, or compounding medical prescriptions, or fixing clocks and locks and bicycles. Just because you like a *person* in a certain occupation is no clear-cut sign that you will like or succeed in the *work* required in that occupation. There have been many occasions

---

[1] From *The Sea Around Us*, by Rachel L. Carson. Copyright © 1950, 1951, 1961 by Rachel L. Carson. Reprinted by permission of Oxford University Press, Inc.

when young people have aspired to be like persons whom they have admired and have followed in their footsteps or in closely allied fields. In these cases, however, the young people have also had some of the skills and abilities held by the persons they admired. There is no rule of thumb, no magic formula, no shortcut to making a wise vocational selection. And, if there were one such easy method, it probably would *not* be based upon whether you admired or liked a person in a certain kind of occupation.[1]

EXERCISE A   In the following two paragraphs the first sentence, the topic sentence, has been omitted. Write in the spaces preceding each paragraph a suitable topic sentence for the paragraph.

A

. . . .

. . . .

. . . .

. . . .

Congress did not declare the independence of the Colonies on the fourth of July, but on the second. John Adams thought at the time that the second of July would forever be considered "the most memorable day in the history of America." Furthermore, only one member of Congress signed the Declaration of Independence on the fourth. Most of the others affixed their signatures on the second of August; some signed later in 1776, and the last, Thomas McKean of Delaware, did not sign until 1777.

B

. . . .

. . . .

. . . .

. . . .

The gangster and detective-story programs give children the impression that our cities are full of gangsters riding around in limousines and "knocking off" other hoodlums and the police. The cowboy films give the impression that the West is a romantic land with a rustler for every "good guy," where every story has a happy ending. The "good guys" always triumph over the bad. Several times a day science fiction programs give false ideas of space travel and of conditions on other planets. As a result of these vivid impressions, children's heads are full of misinformation, and their real lives seem dull in comparison to life in the television world.

[1]From *Points for Decision,* Revised Edition, by Harold J. Mahoney and T. L. Engle, published by Harcourt Brace Jovanovich, Inc. Reprinted by permission of T. L. Engle.

THE ORDER OF IDEAS IN A PARAGRAPH

Always when you plan a paragraph, you must face the problem of arranging the ideas in a clear and logical order. Having written your topic sentence, you then give the facts or reasons which support it. When you are writing a story or describing how to do something, the problem of arranging your ideas is not difficult because your method is chronological—the order in which events happen. When you write a paragraph to give information or to persuade the reader, however, you must give careful attention to arrangement. Here are two principles to guide you:

1. Keep together all sentences pertaining to the same idea.
2. Place early in the paragraph those ideas which are necessary if a person is to understand later ideas in the same paragraph.

EXERCISE B   The sentences in the following two paragraphs have been numbered and printed out of their proper order. In the spaces at the right, place the numbers of the sentences in the order you think the sentences should follow in a well-arranged paragraph. Naturally, your first step is to find the topic sentence and place its number first.

A

1. For one thing, despite the objections of the Administration and most business leaders, we must move to a shorter work week or work year, combined, if desired, with multiple-shift operations.   ....

2. If the national goal is to minimize technological displacement and unemployment without going back to horse-and-buggy production methods, then a variety of possible policies would achieve optimum employment.   ....

3. For another, young people should be required to stay in school longer.

4. This would keep more people employed and would prevent expensive equipment from standing idle.

5. This requirement, combined with an earlier retirement age, would cut persons off from both ends of the labor force, thereby reducing the number of job seekers.[1]

B

1. They worked in congregate shops under strict rules of silence.   ....

2. Solitary night cells cared for the prisoners when not at work.   ....

3. Eyes were to be kept downcast.   ....

4. There was to be no communication whatever.   ....

[1] Adapted from "Automation and Joblessness" by William Glazier in the August 1962 issue of *Atlantic Monthly*. Reprinted by permission of the author.

5. The Auburn system, developed in the 1820's, was the result of New .... York State's experience with its new penitentiary in the upstate .... city. ....

6. Lock-step marching to and from meals and shops was devised.

7. The income from sales of products of the shops was to go toward paying the prison's expenses, an item of the Auburn system not to be ignored.[1]

WRITING ASSIGNMENT Write a carefully constructed informational paragraph (150 words) stating what you hope to accomplish in the next ten years. This is a personal subject about which you undoubtedly have many ideas. Begin with a topic sentence which states the central idea of the paragraph. Plan a logical arrangement of your ideas. This is to be a serious, formal piece of writing, demonstrating good paragraph structure.

You cannot, of course, tell in one paragraph everything you have included in your own ten-year plan. If necessary, you can limit the paragraph to your vocational plans or to your educational, athletic, or social plans. Perhaps you can find an original way of presenting the subject. For example, you might describe yourself, your situation, ten years from now. Questions you may wish to consider:

1. Where do I hope to be living?
2. What kind of work will I be doing?
3. What education will I have had?
4. Will I be married? when? and how many children?
5. What community activities will I be taking a part in?
6. How much traveling will I have done?
7. Will I have had experience in any of the military services?
8. What will my daily routine be?
9. What specific successes do I hope to have achieved?
10. What future will I be looking forward to ten years hence?

Developing the Paragraph

This lesson describes three common methods of developing an idea into a paragraph. The paragraph idea, which is stated in the opening (topic) sentence, may be developed by one of the following methods:

1. by giving details (these may be facts or examples or both)
2. by giving reasons supported by details
3. by drawing a comparison or a contrast supported by details

[1] Adapted from *Dreamers of the American Dream* by Stewart H. Holbrook. Copyright © 1957 by Stewart H. Holbrook. Reprinted by permission of Doubleday & Company, Inc.

Note the importance of *details* in developing a paragraph. If you fail to have enough details (additional information and ideas) to develop your topic, your paragraph will be "thin." A thin paragraph is usually one in which the writer, for lack of material, merely restates the topic sentence several times in different words. *The topic is not developed.*

THIN PARAGRAPH

When you have answered candidly a number of key questions, you will know better whether or not you should seek a college education. Why do you want to go to college? Is it for social reasons, or are you genuinely interested in learning? Have you enough money? Have you the ability to do college work? Are you enthusiastic about going to college? When you have answered these questions honestly, you will have a better idea of whether college is for you.

DEVELOPED PARAGRAPH

When you have answered candidly a number of key questions, you will know better whether or not you should seek a college education. Why do you want to go to college? If you are going for social reasons, such as to keep up with your friends or to have fun, you had better think again. College is hard work. Most college freshmen find they have to curtail their social life quite drastically in order to get their work done. Have you enough money? You should be able to pay your full expenses if necessary for at least the first semester without having to get a job. The strain of holding a job may so affect your studies that you will not be able to keep up scholastically, especially during your first year. Has your high school record been good enough to suggest that you have the ability to do college work? Since many colleges accept only those applicants who have been in the upper half or third of their high school class, college standards are considerably higher than high school standards. One college found that 71 per cent of its students who had a B average in high school were graduated, but only 16 per cent of those who had a C average in high school got their degrees. Finally, are you enthusiastic about going to college? If not, maybe you will be better off in a job for a year or until your enthusiasm increases enough to remove any doubts.

The use of facts is the most commonly employed method of paragraph development. It is rarely found in a pure form, however, except in informational writing. More often the facts are used to support an idea, an opinion, or a reason.

The following paragraphs illustrate the methods of paragraph development.

PARAGRAPH DEVELOPED BY EXAMPLES

Topic sentence

Restatements of topic sentence

Example 1

Example 2

Example 3

To most Hollywood executives, the safest stories still seem to be those which do the people's dreaming for them. Reverie by experts, a silent star once summed it up. Away from your troubles, away from your punch-in-punch-out monotony, you sit there in the enveloping darkness and let De Mille or some other genius of mediocrity spin out for you a million-dollar dream. The homely secretary takes off her glasses and blossoms into a beautiful woman and ideal mate for the boss. The rich and spoiled but beautiful heiress meets her match in an even more headstrong man of the people. The efficient and successful career woman who has forgotten that she is a woman is reminded of the fact by a forceful gent who puts her back in the home, where, it turns out, she wanted to be all along. Just in the nick of time, the villain is caught, the game is won, the show goes on.[1]

—BUDD SCHULBERG

PARAGRAPH DEVELOPED BY REASONS SUPPORTED BY DETAILS

It is "deep-freezing" that has really rung down the curtain on American cookery. Nothing is improved by the process. I have yet to taste a deep-frozen victual that measures up, in flavor, to the fresh, unfrosted original. And most foods, cooked or uncooked, are destroyed in the deep freeze for all people of sense and sensibility. Vegetables with crisp and crackling texture emerge as mush, slippery and stringy as hair nets simmered in Vaseline. The essential oils that make peas peas—and cabbage cabbage—must undergo fission and fusion in freezers. Anyhow, they vanish. Some meats turn to leather. Others to wood pulp. Everything, pretty much, tastes like the mosses of tundra, dug up in midwinter. Even the appearance changes, often-times. Handsome comestibles you put down in the summer come out looking very much like the corpses of woolly mammoths recovered from the last Ice Age.[2] —PHILIP WYLIE

PARAGRAPH DEVELOPED BY COMPARISON SUPPORTED BY DETAILS

The airplane still lacks the secret quality which makes a car so easy to drive—the tendency to go straight unless *commanded* to turn. You have to *make* a car turn by considerable force on the wheel; to keep it turning, you have to keep holding the wheel deflected; and the moment you release the wheel, the car straightens out. The airplane now has the same stability *on the ground,* but not yet in the air. In flight, the airplane always wants to go into a turn, unprovoked by the pilot, to one side or the other. And it won't come out of itself: if allowed its head, it goes into a descending spiral. So, to fly straight, the pilot must nudge the airplane every few seconds by small but positive actions on the controls. If he looks down at his map a little too long, he will, on looking up, find himself in a banked turn, nose-down.[3]

—WOLFGANG LANGEWIESCHE

EXERCISE Read each of the following paragraphs. In the space before each, write the letter of the method by which you think the paragraph is developed: (*a*) by examples, (*b*) by reasons supported by details, (*c*) by drawing a comparison or contrast supported by details.

A

. . . . . Blind college students use recordings and human readers in about equal proportion. There are advantages and disadvantages in both methods. The

---

[1] An excerpt from "Movies in America" by Budd Schulberg which appeared in *The Atlantic Monthly,* November 1947 issue. Reprinted by permission of the Ad Schulberg Agency.
[2] Excerpt from "Science Has Spoiled My Supper" by Philip Wylie in the April 1954 issue of *The Atlantic Monthly.* Copyright 1954 by The Atlantic Monthly Company. Reprinted by permission of Harold Ober Associates Incorporated.
[3] From "The Revolution in Small Plane Flying" by Wolfgang Langewiesche. Copyright © 1960, by *Harper's* Magazine. Reprinted by permission of the author.

advantage of human readers is that they are present to answer the student's questions and to discuss the lessons. The disadvantages are that the method is expensive, since the human readers are usually paid; the reading may not be top quality; the readers are not there at any moment when the student wants to study; they cannot be expected to repeat passages again and again. In contrast, the advantages of the recorded book are that it is expertly read; it can be played at any time and as often as the student wishes; and it is free.[1]

B

. . . . . The test to be applied, when a new word is suggested or it is sought to give an old word a new meaning, is this: Does the change enrich the language? The easiest and silliest way in which to impoverish the language is to misuse a good existing word that conveys a clear and precise meaning and thereby to destroy that meaning and render the word useless. This is what Americans have done by using "alibi" when they mean "excuse." An alibi can never be an excuse, and an excuse can never be an alibi. A man pleads an alibi when he denies that he did an act and says that he could not have done it, since he was elsewhere (alibi) at the time. By an excuse, on the other hand, he admits the act, but says there was a good reason for it. The distinction should really not be too difficult for the ordinary intelligence to grasp. The misuse is a barbarism which has made the language poorer by depriving it of a once-useful word. It is like spoiling a chisel by using it as a screwdriver. It is linguistic murder.[2]

C

. . . . . If independent schools are today less vulnerable because of their alleged "snobbishness," this is because they are doing everything in their power to avoid this sin. They would like to feel that their only real aristocracy is that of intellect. Unquestionably the policy of admitting applicants primarily for their demonstrated intelligence and of offering financial assistance to brilliant but indigent candidates has helped to eliminate the opulent "playboy" and the Social Register drone. A school in which more than one-third of the pupils are receiving financial aid towards their education and in which no student is actually paying the full budgeted tuition costs can hardly be regarded as "exclusive." The leading schools, furthermore, are acutely sensitive to any charge of racial or religious bigotry. And indeed they are usually democratic in the sense that no students in the undergraduate body receive special concessions except those they have earned through open and honest competition.[3]

[1] Adapted from "The Talented Blind" by Burnham Carter in the August 18, 1962 issue of *Saturday Review*. Reprinted by permission of *Saturday Review/World*.

[2] From "You Americans Are Murdering the Language" by Lord Conesford, from the July 13, 1957 issue of *The Saturday Evening Post*, © 1957 by The Curtis Publishing Company. Reprinted with permission from The Saturday Evening Post.

[3] Adapted from "Golden Days for Independent Schools" by Claude M. Fuess in the August 18, 1962 issue of *Saturday Review*. Reprinted by permission of *Saturday Review/World*.

WRITING ASSIGNMENT The writing assignment in Lesson 85 was a one-paragraph composition about what you expect to be doing ten years hence. To write that composition you had to use your imagination. The topic for the present writing assignment is, in a sense, the reverse of that one. You are to look back over your years in senior high school. You may, if you wish, include your junior high years, too.

The paragraph may be written to fulfill one of several possible purposes, the purpose being made clear in the topic sentence.

1. You may write an evaluation of your personal development during these years. How much have you matured? In what ways are you a different person now from the person you were in the ninth grade, for instance? Are there respects in which you think you have changed for the worse or for the better? Such a paragraph, although entirely personal, should be as objective and honest as possible.

2. You may wish to discuss how you would do things differently if you had the privilege of living these years over again. Would you have made some decisions differently? Would you have cultivated different friends? Would you have devoted more or less time to your studies?

3. You may wish to tell about a single influence (a person, an event, an institution, or a school course) that brought about a significant change in you or in your life.

4. You may prefer to present a critical opinion of some aspect of your life in the past years, showing ways in which this side of your life has been unsatisfactory. The side of your life which you analyze might concern your school, your community, your church, your social life, or a similar situation.

5. You could probably write an interesting paragraph describing your accomplishments (or failures) in one phase of your life: school activities, clubs, hobbies, academic work, sports, jobs, and so on.

When you have decided what you wish to say about your immediate past, write a topic sentence which says it clearly. Then *develop* the idea in 150–200 words, giving details (facts, examples, reasons) in support of it. The important thing is to include enough details to develop the topic adequately.

Using Transitional Expressions

One of the difficulties young writers frequently encounter is that of moving smoothly from one idea to another within a paragraph. The use of *transitional expressions* is an aid in solving this problem.

Study the two common types of transitional expressions listed below.

1. Words which refer to the person or idea just mentioned:

he	she	they	that	those	it
his	her	this	these	them	

2. Words or expressions which connect ideas:

accordingly	for example	next
again	for instance	on the contrary
also	furthermore	on the other hand
although	hence	otherwise
as a result	however	second
at last	in addition	similarly
at the same time	in conclusion	since
besides	in fact	then
consequently	in short	therefore
equally important	likewise	thus
finally	moreover	too
first	nevertheless	whereas

EXERCISE   In the following passage, underline the transitional expressions—single words or groups of words like those on page 212 and above. Find at least ten.

At some point in the next thirty-six hours, millions of hapless Americans laboring to meet tomorrow's midnight deadline for filing tax returns are likely to imagine the Revenue Agent looking over their shoulder—all-knowing, all-seeing, catching every slip of arithmetic, sensing somehow every dollar forgotten or unreported.

This image of the Revenue Agents' professional abilities is 96 per cent correct. But the area in which they miss is expensive. Tax experts believe that nearly $25 billion of taxable income is unreported every year. Of this sum, about $5 billion belongs to farmers, they think, and $7 billion to small business owners and professional people. Unreported wages and salaries account for another $6.5 billion, and nearly $4 billion in dividends and interest is not reported. The balance is in rents, royalties, capital gains, pensions and annuities.

How does the tax on these multi-billion-dollar sums manage to escape the 57,000 employees of the Internal Revenue Service? For a start, remember that the total is composed of millions of tiny fragments scattered through some 96,000,000 tax returns. Remember also that our system is, as Justice Robert H. Jackson once said, "taxation by confession." Unless a tax return is audited, the Government must rely on what taxpayers state their incomes, expenses, and taxes to be. Except where taxes are withheld, the taxpayers' honesty, memory, and records are crucial. Under-reporting, therefore, occurs mainly in activities in which cash transactions are frequent, where record-keeping is poor, and where there is no withholding.

Many doctors, for example, receive considerable portions of their income in cash. Overworked or constantly on the move, they may be unable to keep meticulous records, and if, inadvertently, they spend some of the cash before they can deposit it in a bank or make a record of it, the Government may be short-changed.

Not all of the under-reporting by professional people is unintentional. Tax prosecutors tell of one doctor who kept a large fishbowl in his office, advising his patients, "$3 in the fishbowl or I'll bill you $5." A dentist was discovered with $27,000 in cash filed away among his patients' X-rays. Another doctor practiced for thirty-five years without ever filing a tax return. Revenue agents could not forgive this oversight, in spite of the fact that during the depression the physician had charged only 75 cents for house calls and office visits and was seldom paid in cash.

The billions of unreported small-business income are also explained by the frequency of cash transactions and the paucity of careful bookkeeping. Corner grocers, for example, may convince themselves that the revenue agent will never know the difference if some of the cash they take in bypasses the cash register and finds its way into their pockets.

Many small businesses, furthermore, tend to pay off other creditors first, leaving the Government to last. Some have even "borrowed" from the taxes they have withheld from their employees, fully intending, perhaps, to restore such money and pay over the correct total to the Government at the proper time. But if, in the meantime, they go bankrupt, Uncle Sam is left holding an empty bag.

Finally, the $6.5 billion of undeclared wages and salaries is believed to be mostly in the hands of casual or transient workers—domestics who work one day a week for several employers, itinerant farm workers, construction workers who float from job to job. "Moonlighters" are also a problem, since there is frequently no withholding of taxes from their second-job earnings.[1]

WRITING ASSIGNMENT This project again calls for only one paragraph. In it you are to demonstrate your command of paragraph structure—topic sentence, full development, the use of transitional words and phrases (see lists on pp. 212–13).

The topic for this paragraph is to be your concept of the ideal wife or the ideal husband. If you think you would like married life, you have undoubtedly thought about the kind of person you would like to marry. Your purpose in writing this paragraph will be to describe and explain the qualities you would look for in a mate. Since the paragraph is to be a list of these qualities, the organization, or order of ideas, presents no serious problem. Be sure, however, to develop the ideas—reasons, details, examples—so that your paragraph will be more fully developed than a mere list.

The following questions may prove helpful in planning your paragraph:

1. Should an ideal mate be like you in personality, interests, background?
2. What personality characteristics do you consider important—ambition, sense of humor, intelligence, kindness, manners, talents?
3. How important are physical characteristics?
4. Is it important to have the same attitudes toward children, parents, money, religion, work?

[1] Adapted from "That Missing 4 Billion in Taxes" by Philip M. Stern, in the April 15, 1962 issue of the *New York Times Magazine*, © 1962 by The New York Times Company. Reprinted by permission.

Outlining the Longer Composition

The Composition of Several Paragraphs You are now familiar with the principles that govern the organization of the paragraph. A composition of several paragraphs is governed by the same principles. Each begins with a statement of the central idea, which is developed in succeeding statements. While the paragraph is built around the topic sentence, the longer composition develops out of what is sometimes called the topic paragraph—often the first one. The paragraphs that follow then present supporting ideas just as the sentences in the paragraph support the topic sentence.

You plan a longer composition in the same way that you plan a paragraph. Begin by writing down your central idea. Then list all ideas you may wish to include. Discard those that are unimportant or do not support your central idea. Finally, in planning the longer composition, make a careful outline.

The outline is important because it helps you to group related ideas under the main ideas that they support. The development of each major idea will probably, though not necessarily, require a paragraph. A two-page composition, for instance, may have three major topics, each developed by a paragraph.

Before you prepare an outline for this lesson, review the rules for outline form.

Rules for Outline Form There are two forms of outline: the *sentence* form and the *topic* form. In the sentence outline, the topics are complete sentences; in the topic outline, the topics are phrases, subordinate clauses, or single words. Because the sentence outline is cumbersome to prepare, it is rarely used. The following rules apply to the topic outline.

1. Place the title above the outline. It is not one of the numbered or lettered topics.
2. The terms *Introduction, Body, Conclusion* should not be included in the outline. They are not topics to be discussed in the composition. They are merely organizational terms in the writer's mind.
3. Use Roman numerals for the main topics. Use letters and numbers for subtopics according to the following arrangement:

STANDARD OUTLINE FORM

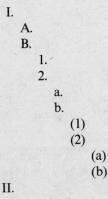

I.
   A.
   B.
      1.
      2.
         a.
         b.
            (1)
            (2)
               (a)
               (b)
II.

4. Indent subtopics so that all letters or numbers of the same kind will come directly under one another in a vertical line.

5. Begin each topic with a capital letter. Do not capitalize other words in a topic unless they are always capitalized. In other words, do not treat a topic as though it were a book title.

INCORRECT   I. Recent Changes in American Policy
CORRECT   I. Recent changes in American policy

6. There must never be, under any topic, a lone subtopic; there must be either two or more subtopics or none at all. Subtopics are divisions of the topic above them. A topic cannot be divided into fewer than two parts.

7. Do not use sentences in a topical outline.

8. As a rule, main topics should be parallel in form, and subtopics under the same topic should be parallel in form. If the first topic in a list is a noun, the others should be nouns; if it is a phrase, the others should be phrases of the same kind.

TOPICS NOT PARALLEL

Moving to a New Neighborhood (title)

Noun and adj. clause —— I. The fact that I lost my old friends

II. My attendance at a new school
    A. New teachers —————————— modifier and noun
    B. Courses are taught differently ———— sentence

Modifier, noun, and phrase III. My acquisition of new friends
    A. Seeking help with new procedures —— gerund, noun, and phrase
    B. Joined groups with similar interests —— participle, noun, and phrase

TOPICS PARALLEL

Moving to a New Neighborhood (title)

I. My loss of old friends

II. My attendance at a new school
    A. New teachers ———
Modifier, noun, and phrase
    B. Different courses ——— modifier and noun

III. My acquisition of new friends
    A. Seeking help with new procedures ——
    B. Joining groups with similar interests —— gerund, noun, and phrase

Once you have prepared your outline, you are ready to begin writing. If, as you write, you decide to alter your plan, change your outline. The outline is not final until the composition has been completed. The important point is that if your composition follows a logical outline, it will be clear.

EXERCISE A   Rewrite the following outline in the spaces provided at the right. Correct all technical errors in numbering, parallel form, capitalization, lone subtopics, arrangement, etc.

A Birthday Party

I. The Guests . . . .

   A. Typical Appearance . . . .

   B. Actions that are typical . . . .

II. The refreshments . . . .

   a. The beverages that are served. . . . .

   B. What food is served . . . .

III. The entertainment . . . .

   1. Games that are played . . . .

   2. Dancing . . . .

      A. records . . . .

   3. Singing songs . . . .

EXERCISE B   Using the spaces provided at the right, arrange the following list of topics in a correctly written outline. The title is included in the list.

clubs   (Title). . . . .

musical organizations   . . . .

Student Council   . . . .

Drama Club   . . . .

band   . . . .

school activities   . . . .

student government groups   . . . .

newspaper   . . . .

orchestra   . . . .

publications   . . . .

Student Court   . . . .

homeroom committee   . . . .

yearbook   . . . .

Photography Club   . . . .

magazine   . . . .

choral groups   . . . .

Hobby Club   . . . .

WRITING ASSIGNMENT   In this assignment you return to the multi-paragraph composition. The composition is to contain at least three paragraphs. Also, it is to be accompanied by an outline with at least three major (Roman numeral) topics and at least two subtopics under each. You will be judged on the form (Rules 1–8, pp. 215–16) as well as on the content of your outline.

The purpose of your composition is to explain something—how to do something or how something was done. The range of topics is great. You may, for example, write an explanation of the decline of colonialism or you may write on how to set up a chemistry experiment.

Develop your explanation by giving facts. Suppose, for example, that you are writing an article on how to sail. The facts you wish to include fall into four groups. Each of these groups will constitute a paragraph. In your outline, then, you will have four major topics. This need not mean, however, that you must limit yourself to four paragraphs, for you may wish to begin with a brief introductory paragraph and to close with a brief concluding paragraph. In this instance, the introductory paragraph might arouse interest by telling a sailing incident or by telling how much fun sailing is if you know how.

How to Sail

I. Controlling the boat
  A. Handling the sheet
  B. Handling the rudder
II. Sailing before the wind
  A. Pleasures
  B. Dangers
III. Changing direction
  A. Coming about
  B. Jibing
IV. Sailing into the wind
  A. Theory of tacking
  B. Practice of tacking

Whether you realize it or not, you are to a certain degree an expert in something. You may be an expert in sewing or cooking or home decoration. You may have a hobby such as photography or making airplane models or rebuilding old cars. You may have special knowledge of the position of catcher on a baseball team or of the openings of the chess masters. Whatever your field of knowledge is, you will do well to choose from it the subject of this composition.

If you prefer, you may write an explanatory article which will be the result of your research and reading. Choose, for example, a topic like "Travel in Outer Space," "Weather Forecasting," or a current political crisis. The *Readers' Guide* and the card catalogue in your library will provide articles and books on the topic, and a little reading will give you the information you need. Do not *copy* your sources, however. Use the information but not the words of articles you read.

Paragraphing the Longer Composition

Paragraphing helps readers. The indention of the first line of a paragraph is a visual signal to readers which tells them that a different aspect of the subject is about to be discussed, that a new point is coming up.

Failure to divide your writing into paragraphs will make it much more difficult for your readers to follow you. By contrast, too many paragraphs will confuse readers who expect sentences to be *grouped* to support an idea, not written each as a separate paragraph.

Paragraph a composition so that the various phases of a subject will stand out clearly. Avoid the overlong and the very short paragraph.

A longer composition usually begins with a short introductory or "topic" paragraph, giving briefly the purpose of the composition or stating the proposition to be argued. The composition may be concluded with another short paragraph which clinches the point of the article. But the composition itself should not be broken up by many short paragraphs, nor should it consist of just one long paragraph.

EXERCISE A Indicate with the sign ¶ where you think paragraph divisions should be made in the following unparagraphed composition. Look for topic sentences which begin paragraphs.

TEACHERS' FAULTS

In our world of complex technology, the quality of education is a matter of great concern. Because teachers are responsible for this education, it is important that we have good teachers. Since they are human, however, even the best teachers occasionally display faults. While I respect and admire my teachers, I would like to describe a few of these faults. One of these faults is a sin of omission. It is a teacher's failure to recognize differences in ability among students. Many good teachers, finding the bright students most interesting, seem to be interested only in their bright pupils. The result is that these students, who really need the teacher least, get most of the attention. The average and slow students, who need the teacher most, are ignored or left to struggle through alone. Another fault of some teachers is giving too much homework and, often, the wrong kind of homework. These teachers seem to forget that students are taking several subjects, not just the one they are teaching. As a result, conscientious students find themselves so overwhelmed by long assignments that they become discouraged or resort to copying. Furthermore, much of the work in a long assignment is repetitious. Students can accomplish as much by doing ten math problems as they can by doing fifteen or twenty. Finally, a teacher's effectiveness is sometimes weakened by an inability to control classes. Students will behave only as well as the teacher requires. If the teacher is lax, even serious students who want to work and learn will fall into bad classroom habits, which prevent learning. Although the students are not free from blame in unruly classes, the principal blame should fall on the teachers. No matter how much teachers know, and no matter how carefully they plan their presentations, their students will not learn unless the teachers can control them.

TRANSITIONS BETWEEN PARAGRAPHS

Make the transition between paragraphs clear and smooth by using a transitional device at the beginning of a paragraph.

There are several ways to achieve smooth transitions between paragraphs.

1. Use a pronoun which refers to a person or an idea just mentioned in the preceding paragraph.
The following pronouns are useful in effecting a transition by this means:

he	this	these	them	it
she	that	those	they	

EXAMPLE   . . . Such, then, were the four charges drawn up against the officers of the firm.

As everyone knows by now, not one of these was ever proved. (The pronoun *these* refers to *charges* in the preceding paragraph.)

2. Refer to the central idea of the preceding paragraph.

EXAMPLE   Only by such drastic measures can we hope to reduce crime in our cities. (The phrase *such drastic measures* refers to measures mentioned in the preceding paragraph.)

3. Use transitional words or expressions such as the following:

accordingly	by contrast	however	similarly
also	consequently	in fact	still
another	finally	likewise	such
as a result	for example	moreover	then
at last	for instance	nevertheless	therefore
at this time	furthermore	otherwise	thus

EXAMPLE   . . . This new communications satellite may be the means of bringing all the peoples of the world close together.

However, censorship by a country of broadcasts from another part of the world would seriously threaten the effectiveness of international television by satellites. (The transitional word *however* links this paragraph to the preceding one.)

EXERCISE B   Assume that each of the following sentences is the first sentence of a paragraph within a longer composition. Draw a line under the words used to effect the transition from what has gone before. In the space at the right of each sentence, name the transitional device.

     a. pronoun
     b. reference to a preceding idea
     c. transitional expression

1. There surely is a hope that this may be the significance of the latest achievement of science.   ....
2. This possibility, though it must be faced, should not be seen too tragically.   ....
3. Our failures, moreover, are always more spectacular than our successes.   ....
4. These are some of the hard facts about human relations.   ....
5. There is only one possible cure for this dangerous situation.   ....
6. On the contrary, there is strong evidence that the students with the highest grades are not the students with the highest ability.   ....
7. Principal victim of this situation is the downtown area of the American city, where parking and traffic are two major problems.   ....
8. This is all very obvious.   ....
9. The second factor is the heterogeneousness of American culture.   ....
10. All these generalizations, however, are of very little help in solving our specific problems.   ....

WRITING ASSIGNMENT   In this writing assignment, you are to write your reactions to a news story in a daily paper. All of us react to items in the news. We may be pleased, angered, irritated, critical, surprised, or simply amused. Examine your daily paper. Find a news item about which you have some opinions and ideas. It may concern anything from international relations to sports, but it should not be trivial. Plan a composition of at least three paragraphs (300–400 words), giving your reactions and your reasons for them. Prepare an outline to be submitted with your composition. Begin each paragraph after the first with a transitional device.

Writing a Logical Argument

  In presenting an argument, you follow a logical thought process which may be called a "line of reasoning." Study the following descriptions of three common types of reasoning. Note the pitfalls in each. This review will help you to see weaknesses in the arguments of those who disagree with you, and it will help you to fashion stronger arguments in favor of your own point of view.

  1. Reasoning by Deduction   When you reason deductively, you start with a general statement, apply it to a particular instance, and *deduce* a conclusion. Deductive reasoning proceeds through three steps which together are called a *syllogism*. The first two steps are premises; the final step is the conclusion based on the premises.

MAJOR PREMISE   No seniors attended yesterday's meeting.
MINOR PREMISE   John is a senior.
CONCLUSION   John did not attend yesterday's meeting.

The conclusion in this syllogism is sound because the major and minor premises are true, and the conclusion follows logically from them.

However, a syllogism may be false. For instance, in the following syllogism, the conclusion is false.

MAJOR PREMISE   All athletes enjoy sports.
MINOR PREMISE   Julia enjoys sports.
CONCLUSION   Julia is an athlete.

Clear thinking will reveal the error here. The major premise does not say that all who enjoy sports are athletes. If it did say so, the conclusion would be logical, but it would still be incorrect because such a major premise is not true.

In deductive reasoning both premises must be true and the conclusion must be logically drawn from them.

2. Reasoning by Induction   When you reason inductively, you gather evidence, and from this evidence you draw a conclusion or generalization. This is the opposite of the deductive method. Scientists reason inductively. They do not make a generalization until they have first gathered sufficient evidence to support it. You reason inductively every day. If you reach into a barrel of apples and draw out twelve apples all of which are rotten, you may generalize that all apples in this barrel are rotten. You may be correct in this generalization or you may be incorrect. The question is whether twelve apples provide a sufficient sampling to warrant your generalization.

Test inductive reasoning by examining the extent of the evidence on which the generalization is based.

A generalization based on insufficient evidence is a *hasty* generalization and is a common fault in reasoning.

Caution: You should realize one important difference between a conclusion reached deductively and a conclusion reached inductively. A conclusion reached deductively can be unquestionably true, provided the premises are true and the reasoning is logical. A conclusion reached inductively, however, usually states only what is *probably* true. For example, if you find that all the twelve apples you took from the barrel are rotten, it is *probably* true that all the other apples in the barrel are rotten, too. Your conclusion about the remaining apples is a *probability,* not a certainty. You could be *absolutely* certain only if you examined every apple in the barrel.

3. Reasoning by Analogy   An *analogy* is a comparison. When you reason by analogy, you base your conclusion on a similarity between two things or two sets of circumstances. The analogy is sound only if there are sufficient points of similarity and no important points of dissimilarity. Is the following analogy sound?

The thirteen American colonies in 1781 formed a federation which ultimately became one nation, the United States of America. The nations of the world today can form a federation which will ultimately become one world, the United Nations.

You recognize, of course, that this is a weak analogy. While there may be some similarities between the situation among the colonies in 1781 and the situation among the nations of the world today, many important differences will occur to you which weaken the analogy.

More often than not, argument by analogy is a weak form of argument. Few analogies are strong enough to warrant a strong conclusion. Analogies never prove anything, but if they are reasonable, they do clarify, and they may convince some people.

Test an argument by analogy by examining the points of similarity and by making sure that there are no important points of dissimilarity.

EXERCISE   Examine carefully the logic of each of the following examples of reasoning. In the first space at the right of each example, tell (by letter) which of the three types of reasoning is represented:

a. deduction   *b.* induction   *c.* analogy

In the second space, write a + if you think the conclusion is sound; write 0 if you think the conclusion is unsound. Be prepared to explain your answers.

	Type of Reasoning	*+ or* 0
1. Children are little animals. Animal trainers know they must hold a whip over their charges. Parents and teachers must hold a whip over children.	. . . . .	. . . . .
2. All American citizens are guaranteed freedom to worship as they please. I am an American citizen. I may worship as I please.	. . . . .	. . . . .
3. George had his pocket picked at the fair. Mother lost her handbag at the fair. I will be robbed if I attend the fair.	. . . . .	. . . . .
4. Every community has a police force to make people obey the laws of the community. Every school should have a police force to make students obey the regulations of the school.	. . . . .	. . . . .
5. Drinking coffee has not hurt my grandfather. At eighty he is in excellent health. Drinking coffee will not hurt me.	. . . . .	. . . . .

6. All students with an 85 average will be excused from examinations. Betty has an 85 average. She will be excused from examinations. . . . .|..

7. People should be paid according to their needs and taxed according to their ability to pay. Ms. Brown is wealthy and she has few expenses. Ms. Brown's income should be lowered and her taxes should be raised. . . . .

8. My father did not go to college. He has been successful in business. Since I intend to go into business, I do not need to go to college. . . . . .

9. In a study made in 1953, it was found that at the time of the study there were 642,156 men and 564,436 women in United States hospitals. American men are "sicklier" than American women. . . . .

10. Course examinations are like hurdles in a race. A runner who fails to leap every hurdle is disqualified and must leave the race. A student who fails to pass every course examination should be disqualified and dropped from school. . . . .

WRITING ASSIGNMENT In writing projects up to now, you have given information, made explanations, and expressed opinions. In the composition you are to write for this lesson, you are also to express opinion, but your purpose goes further. You are going to try to persuade or convince your reader to adopt your attitude toward the subject. The result will be an article presenting an argument. Newspaper editorials on controversial issues, political speeches, and legal briefs require this kind of writing.

In preparing your article, follow three steps:

1. State the proposition you intend to argue.
2. List the arguments you can use in support of the proposition.
3. Assemble evidence (facts, authoritative opinions, and so on) in support of the arguments, and list the evidence as subtopics under each major argument. The result will be an outline.

In every school, as in every community and organization, debatable issues constantly arise. As a student and as a citizen you will often find it necessary to take a stand on these issues. When you adopt a pro or a con position, you should be ready to argue in favor of your position. The subject you choose for an argumentative article will be easier to handle if it is a debatable subject currently being discussed among your acquaintances, a subject on which you have heard many arguments. Government and politics are always good sources for debatable issues.

Avoid subjects which are pointless or purely personal, like "summer is a better season than winter." Avoid also subjects which are matters of fact and therefore not arguable. Such subjects can be settled by investigation. For instance, topics like "the cost of living is rising" or "the comic books are more popular than any other reading matter" are not suitable for argument because they are matters of fact.

Suggested Topics   The topics listed below are, in general, old favorites, yet they are still good subjects for argument. They are phrased as questions. You will answer the question either affirmatively or negatively and phrase your proposition accordingly.

SCHOOL

Should seniors enjoy special privileges?
Should students help decide a school's curriculum?
Is homework merely wasteful busywork?

GENERAL

Is personality more important to success than brains?
Is money essential to happiness?
Should all guns be licensed?

GOVERNMENT AND POLITICS

Which branch of the government should exercise the most power—the executive, the legislative, or the judicial?
Should capital punishment be completely abolished?
Should the government subsidize educational TV?

Write an article arguing one side of a debatable issue. State first which proposition you intend to support. Outline your arguments and your proof. Test your reasoning to be sure your conclusions are sound. Pay special attention to paragraphing and to the transitions between paragraphs. Write at least three paragraphs (approximately 400 words).

Letter Writing

This lesson provides a review of the characteristics of a good business letter. The exercises will give you practice in writing two common types of business letters: the letter of inquiry and the letter of application.

The Parts of a Business Letter First, you should review the six parts of a business letter. As you read the following, refer to the sample on the facing page.

1. *The heading.* Placed in the upper right-hand corner about two inches below the top of the page, the heading gives in three lines the following information:

Top line—writer's street address	950 University Circle
Middle line—city, state, zip code	Duluth, Minnesota 55811
Bottom line—date	February 6, 1977

2. *The inside address.* Placed at the left margin one-half inch below the heading, the inside address gives on separate lines: the name, if known, of the individual to whom you are writing; the name of the firm; the street address of the addressee; the city, the state, and zip code of the addressee. (There is no comma between the state and the zip code.)

The individual's name is always preceded by a title: Mr., Ms., Miss, Mrs., Professor, etc.

3. *The salutation.* Placed at the left margin below the inside address, the salutation is followed by a colon (:).

a. To a firm—Gentlemen: Ladies: (for an all-female concern)
If the firm or group you are writing to is composed of men and women, the traditional salutation is Gentlemen:. (See sample letter of inquiry.)
b. To a person whose name you know—Dear Mr. Bowles: Dear Mrs. Roth:
When writing to a woman who does not identify herself as single or married, you may use *Ms.* in the salutation. You may also address a man or woman by using both their first and last names in the salutation.
c. To an official whose name you do not know—Dear Dean of Admissions: Dear Treasurer:

4. *The body of the letter.* The body, or main part of the letter, begins below the salutation, indented an inch, or five typewriter spaces.

5. *The closing.* The closing follows the body of the letter and begins just to the right of the middle of the page. It is followed by a comma.

EXAMPLES Yours truly, Very truly yours, Sincerely yours,

6. *The signature.* This signature, handwritten, comes directly below the closing. It is never preceded by *Mr.* or *Ms.* An unmarried woman may choose to place (Miss) before her name. A married woman may write, in parentheses, below her signature,

her married name. In typewritten letters, the writer's name is usually typed below the signature:

EXAMPLES   Very truly yours,

Margaret Smith

(Miss) Margaret Smith

Very truly yours,

Jane Simmons

Jane Simmons
(Mrs. George Simmons)

Heading

               14 Cambridge Avenue
               Sandusky, Ohio 44870
               February 20, 1977

Inside Address

Admissions Office
University of Michigan
Ann Arbor, Michigan 48104

Salutation

Gentlemen:

Body of letter

    Since submitting my application for admission to the University of Michigan, I have learned that the tuition fee for out-of-state students has been raised. I should like to know what the new fee will be. I should also like to have any available information on freshman scholarships and part-time job opportunities in Ann Arbor.

Closing

               Very truly yours,

Signature

               Maureen McKenzie

               Maureen McKenzie

Sample letter of inquiry

Margins A letter must always be centered on the page; that is, there should be ample margins of equal width at either side and above and below the letter. To make the letter attractive in appearance, leave wide margins. A letter placed off center or crowded to the edges makes a very poor "picture."

Stationery Write business letters on white stationery, either your personal stationery or standard typewriting paper. Do not write on both sides of the paper. If necessary, continue your letter on a second page, but be sure to have several lines on the second page, not just the closing and signature, for instance.

The Letter of Inquiry   Written usually to get information, the letter of inquiry, like all business letters, must be clear and brief, as in the sample letter on page 227.

EXERCISE A   Assume that you are writing a research paper. Write a letter of inquiry to a likely source of information on your topic, requesting any free material available.

The Letter of Application   As you prepare to graduate from high school, you become vitally interested in getting a job, either a permanent position or summer employment. Employers who wish to do some preliminary "weeding out" of candidates before scheduling personal interviews frequently require a letter of application from anyone interested in the position. This letter not only determines who will be interviewed but often determines who will actually get the job. It is an important letter.

Study the following suggestions concerning the letter of application, and read carefully the sample letter on the facing page.

1. Make your opening paragraph a concise statement of the position for which you are applying and how you learned about it.

2. Give the facts about yourself which a prospective employer would want to know: age, education, experience.

3. Emphasize any qualities you possess which you think make you a good person for this position, but do not appear boastful or conceited.

4. Give references (usually three) with their addresses. If you have worked at other jobs, include a former employer among your references. Other references may be an adult friend of your family or a teacher or your pastor or school principal. Always ask permission before giving a person's name as a reference.

5. At the end of the letter, express your interest in a personal interview at the employer's convenience.

6. Before copying your letter in final form, check it carefully for errors in spelling, grammar, neatness, form, etc. Be sure it will make a favorable impression.

EXERCISE B   Imagine a position for which you would like to apply, either now or at some future date. Following the preceding suggestions concerning the letter of application, write a letter of application for this position. If you prefer, you may select from the Help Wanted columns of your daily newspaper a job you would like to have and write a letter of application for the job.

126 Maple Avenue
Hanover, New Jersey 07936
May 10, 1977

Mr. Frederick Johnson, Director
Camp Towanda
Sussex, New Jersey 07461

Dear Mr. Johnson:

Please consider me an applicant for the position of counselor advertised in today's _Jersey Journal_.

I am 17 years of age and will graduate from Hanover High School next month. I have varsity letters in the three major sports and was co-captain of the football team last fall. I am very much interested in athletics and hope to make a career of coaching and physical education work.

For the past two summers I have been junior counselor at Camp Borne in Rutland, Vermont. I assisted the counselor in charge of baseball and swimming. I am not returning to Camp Borne this year because the camp's enrollment is down. I gained valuable experience in working with boys during the past winter when I assisted with after-school sports at the Willis Country Day School here. My experience has shown me that I enjoy working with younger boys, and I believe I have been successful in getting along with them.

The following persons have given me permission to submit their names as references:

Mr. Albert Lockhart, Director, Camp Borne, Rutland, Vermont
The Reverend James Lutz, Hanover Congregational Church, Hanover, New Jersey
Mr. Warren Thompson, Principal, Hanover High School, Hanover, New Jersey

I shall be glad to come to your home at any time for a personal interview.

Sincerely yours,

Wayne Sloan

Wayne Sloan

Sample letter of application

Envelope The address on the envelope of a business letter should be identical with the inside address. Place the address just below the middle of the envelope and begin it a little to the left of center. Place the return address in the upper left-hand corner in three lines: your name; street address; city, state, and zip code. Turn back to page 227 and compare the model business letter with its envelope below. Notice, in the return address on the envelope, that a title (Mr., Ms., Miss, Mrs.) is not used before the writer's name.

```
Maureen McKenzie
14 Cambridge Avenue
Sandusky, Ohio 44870

                           Admissions Office
                           University of Michigan
                           Ann Arbor, Michigan 48104
```

Envelope for a business letter

The Research Paper: Finding Sources

Lessons 92–95 are devoted to one composition assignment, the writing of a long formal paper (1,500–2,000 words) giving information gathered from a number of sources. In preparing your research paper, or source theme, you will become acquainted with some of the important techniques generally found effective in this kind of work; you will renew your acquaintance with library tools; and you will demonstrate, as a kind of culmination of your training in writing, the skills of organization and composition at your command. The entire project will require several weeks of work and should result in a paper in which you can take real pride.

Before beginning work, study the following list of the steps in preparing a research paper. The list will give you a clear idea of the nature and proportions of the job ahead.

STEPS IN WRITING A RESEARCH PAPER

1. Select an appropriate subject.
2. Prepare a working bibliography.
3. Make a preliminary outline.
4. Read and take notes.
5. Organize notes and write a final outline.
6. Write the first draft with footnotes.
7. Write the final draft and final bibliography.

Step 1. Select an appropriate subject.

An appropriate subject is one on which your library has enough material and one that is limited enough for treatment in a paper of 1,500 to 2,000 words (roughly eight to ten typewritten pages). It is better to make a deep study of a narrow subject than a shallow study of a broad subject.

The following areas for research are very broad. They are intended only as indications of the kind of subject matter which lends itself to treatment in a research paper. Whatever general area you choose must be broken down into more limited subareas, one of which may be suitable for a research paper.

Areas for Research

HISTORY	Life in a medieval castle, early settlements in America, nineteenth-century imperialism, the great religions, great historical documents, the colonial village, history of dress or costume, early automobiles, the League of Nations, NATO, the UN, the 1890's, the tariff, Battle of Gettysburg, American foreign policy, the Cuban crisis of 1962, collectivism in Russia, the United States' Bicentennial
LITERATURE	Greek drama, Elizabethan theater, novels of Charlotte Brontë, American regional literature, American myths, realism in liter-

231

ature, folk ballads, modern poetry, modern satirical writers, history of the short story, women novelists

MODERN PROBLEMS   Political problems in Africa, Latin America, or elsewhere, population growth, censorship, education, unemployment, farm price supports, the Welfare State, foreign aid, the world's food shortage, the spread of disease, racial equality, conservation, pollution, oil and international relations

SCIENCE   Space travel, rocketry, modern telescopes, nuclear power, new sources of energy, diet, food substitutes, science and agriculture, computers, research on cancer, heart disease (or another disease), synthetics, harnessing the sun, controlling the weather

THE ARTS   Modern painting or sculpture, jazz, modern dance, ballet, Elizabethan music, architecture today, grand opera, great portrait painters, art in advertising, home decoration, antiques, fashion designers

The following example shows you how to proceed in limiting a subject.

GENERAL AREA   Modern problems
SPECIFIC SUBJECT   Conservation
SPECIFIC PHASE   Air and water pollution
LIMITATION   Air pollution in our cities
FINAL LIMITATION   How can air pollution in our cities be controlled?

Submit to your teacher for approval the subject you finally choose. You will be told whether you have limited it sufficiently.

Step 2. Prepare a working bibliography.

Before you can start reading on your subject, you must prepare a list of the sources available to you. This list of sources (articles, books, pamphlets) is your *bibliography*. To prepare this bibliography you will use familiar library tools: for magazine articles, the *Readers' Guide to Periodical Literature;* for books, the card catalogue; for pamphlets and clippings, the vertical file. This first bibliography will consist of all likely books and articles you can discover. With it as a guide, you will start your reading. You may find that some of these possible sources are useless to you, and so you will eventually remove them from your bibliography. Because the purpose of this bibliography is to help you while working on your paper, it is referred to as the "working bibliography" to distinguish it from the final bibliography you will write later. The final bibliography is a list of only those sources you actually used in your paper.

The efficient way to prepare a working bibliography is to write each source (article, book, pamphlet) on a separate 3 × 5-inch index card. The information put on a card must be complete. Be sure to get all the necessary information now so that later you will not have to look it up again.

BIBLIOGRAPHICAL INFORMATION
FOR A MAGAZINE OR NEWSPAPER ARTICLE

1. Author (last name first) unless the article is unsigned
2. Title of article (in quotes)

232

3. Name of magazine (underlined)
4. Volume and page number as in the *Readers' Guide* listing (not necessary for newspaper articles)
5. Date

All this information will be found in the *Readers' Guide.*

The Readers' Guide The *Readers' Guide* lists, every two weeks (monthly in July and August), the articles in more than a hundred magazines. The articles are listed according to their subject and their author, not according to title. If you are writing your research paper on a topic of current interest, you will start work by turning to the *Readers' Guide* and looking up the subject you are to write on. By looking through all recent issues and the cumulative volumes of recent years, you will be able to locate quickly all magazine articles on your subject. Even if you are writing on a historical subject, the *Readers' Guide* may be helpful because many current magazines contain articles on historical subjects.

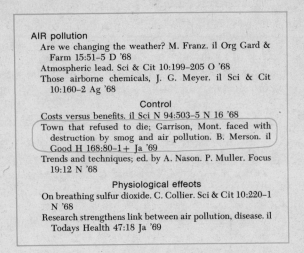

AIR pollution
Are we changing the weather? M. Franz. il Org Gard & Farm 15:51–5 D '68
Atmospheric lead. Sci & Cit 10:199–205 O '68
Those airborne chemicals, J. G. Meyer. il Sci & Cit 10:160–2 Ag '68

Control
Costs versus benefits. il Sci N 94:503–5 N 16 '68
Town that refused to die; Garrison, Mont. faced with destruction by smog and air pollution. B. Merson. il Good H 168:80–1+ Ja '69
Trends and techniques; ed. by A. Nason. P. Muller. Focus 19:12 N '68

Physiological effects
On breathing sulfur dioxide. C. Collier. Sci & Cit 10:220–1 N '68
Research strengthens link between air pollution, disease. il Todays Health 47:18 Ja '69

Part of a page from Readers' Guide[1]

Notice in the sample entries from the *Readers' Guide* how the information about a magazine article is given. The entry circled in red appears under the subject heading "Air pollution" and the subheading "Control." The entry gives the title of the article, "Town that Refused to Die: Garrison, Mont., Faced with Destruction by Smog and Air Pollution," and the name of the author, B. Merson. It then tells, in order, that the illustrated (il) article appeared in *Good Housekeeping*, volume 168, pages 80–81+, for January 1969. (The + shows that the article runs beyond page 81.) These facts should appear on your working bibliography card for this article as illustrated on the following page.

---

[1]Material from the *Readers' Guide to Periodical Literature* is reproduced by permission of the H. W. Wilson Company.

Merson, B.
"Town That Refused to Die: Garrison, Mont.,
Faced with Destruction by Smog and Air
Pollution,"
Good Housekeeping, 168:80-1+, January, 1969

⑤

Sample bibliography card for a magazine article

Each card in your working bibliography should be numbered. Note the number in the upper right-hand corner of the sample card. The importance of this number will be explained later (see p. 238).

The Card Catalogue Every library book (except fiction) is represented in the library's card catalogue by at least three cards: an author card, a title card, and one or more subject cards. The top line on the card tells you which kind it is: the author's name appears at the top of an author card; the title of the book at the top of a title card; the subject about which the book is written at the top of the subject card. When you are beginning your research, you will be interested principally in the subject card.

614.7   AIR – POLLUTION
H   **Herber, Lewis.**
    Crisis in our cities. Englewood Cliffs, N. J., Prentice-Hall
[1965]

    xii, 239 p. illus., maps. 22 cm.

    Bibliographical references included in "Notes" (p. 201–223)

    1. Air — Pollution. 2. water — Pollution. 3. City and town life. I. Title.

RA566.114   614.7   65–12920

Library of Congress   [6517]

Sample card catalogue subject card

Several important items of information appear on this card. The call number in the upper left-hand corner is the classification number of the book according to the Dewey decimal system of classification used in most libraries. Since books are arranged on the shelves according to their classification, you can tell from the call number on which shelf you will find the book. Write the call number in the upper left-hand corner of your bibliography card.

1. Call number (Write in upper left-hand corner.)
2. Author or editor, last name first (Indicate the editor by placing *ed.* after the name.)
3. Title (underlined) and volume if the book is in several volumes
4. Place of publication
5. Publisher
6. Year of publication

614.7
H
Herber, Lewis
Crisis in Our Cities
Englewood Cliffs, N.J., Prentice-Hall, 1965

⑦

Sample bibliography card for a book

The Vertical File In most libraries, the librarians keep on file a vast amount of valuable material in pamphlet form. The pamphlet material usually represents publications of the government, of industrial firms, of private foundations, and of radio and television forums. The librarians also file important newspaper clippings.

BIBLIOGRAPHICAL INFORMATION FOR A PAMPHLET

The bibliographical information for a pamphlet is essentially the same as that for a book. Of course, since pamphlets are not indexed in the *Readers' Guide* or catalogued, you will have to get the information directly from the pamphlet itself in the vertical file. Naturally, there will be no call number. Many pamphlets are part of a series and so have a series title and number. Some may also have a volume number. On your bibliography card, enclose the name of the series in quotation marks and enclose this and the number of the pamphlet in parentheses.

The Effects of Air Pollution
Washington, D.C., U.S. Department of Health, Education, and Welfare, Public Health Service, 1967
("Public Health Service Publication" No. 1556)

⑮

Sample bibliography card for a pamphlet (author not given)

EXERCISE Using the following data, write out on 3 × 5-inch cards the proper items of information in correct order and form. If you do not have 3 × 5-inch cards, rule spaces on separate sheets of papers.

A. From the *Readers' Guide:*[1]

> bibliog Science 159:1437–40 Mr 29 '68
> Anti-smog gadgets on your car. il Changing T 22:31–3 Ap '68
> Atmospheric particulates: specific surface areas and densities. M. Corn and others. bibliog Science 159:1350–1 Mr 22 '68
> Congress and conservation: air quality act is top 1967 achievement. C. H. Callison. Audubon, 70:56 Ja '68
> Easy method of measuring acidic air pollutants; excerpt from Scientific experi-

> Mike Frome; air pollution and industrial development. M. Frome. Am For 74:5+ Ja '68.
> Reporter at large. E. Iglauer. il New Yorker 44:51–2+ Ap 13 '68
> Urban haze: the extent of automotive contribution. W. E. Buchan and R. J. Charlson. bibliog il Science 159:192–3 Ja 12 '68
>   *See* also
> Smog
>   Control

B. From the card catalogue:

> 628.5
>   C
>
> Carr, Donald Eaton.
>   The breath of life. New York, Norton, 1965. 175p.

> 628.168
>   P
>
> Perry, John.
>   Our polluted world; can man survive?
> New York, Watts, 1967.
>   213p.

---

[1] Material from the *Readers' Guide to Periodical Literature* is reproduced by permission of the H. W. Wilson Company.

C. The cover of a pamphlet from the vertical file:[1]

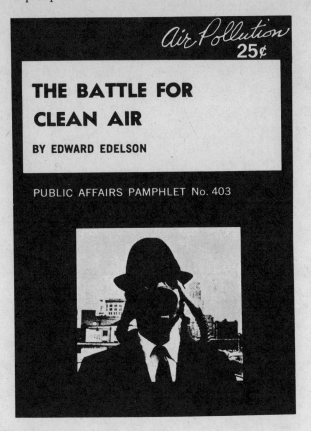

Air Pollution
25¢

THE BATTLE FOR CLEAN AIR

BY EDWARD EDELSON

PUBLIC AFFAIRS PAMPHLET No. 403

LESSON 93

The Research Paper: Outlining and Note-Taking

Step 3. Make a preliminary outline.

After you have consulted a few of your sources, you will have a general idea of the various topics you will want to cover in your paper. In a brief outline, write down the probable divisions of the paper so far as you are able to foresee them. This outline is only preliminary and is partly the result of guesswork, but it is necessary for use in note-taking.

Step 4. Read and take notes.

Notes on the reading in your sources should be written on index cards perhaps a size larger (4 × 6 inches) than the cards used for your working bibliography. At the top of

[1]From "The Battle for Clean Air" by Edward Edelson, published in 1967 by the Public Affairs Committee, Inc. Reprinted by permission of the publisher.

237

a note card, write the topic from your preliminary outline to which the notes on the card will pertain. This topic is commonly referred to as a "slug." Each note card thus contains information about one topic only, and each card bearing the same slug should contain notes from one source only. Thus you may have many cards with the same slug at the top, each one giving additional information about the topic and usually representing a different source. When you have finished taking your notes, you can easily organize your paper by putting together all note cards bearing the same slug.

Before or after each note, give the number of the page from which the note was taken. Later on you will need the page number in writing footnotes.

Legislation
The 1967 bill required that all 1968 private cars must be equipped with a 50% effective control device. (p. 76)
"The car population, however, keeps growing and there are no such regulations for used cars — generally the worst offenders."
(p. 77)

⑦

Sample note card

In the upper right-hand corner of each note card, write the number of the source you are reading. This is the number in the upper right-hand corner of the working bibliography card you made out for this source. Using numbers in this way frees you from the time-consuming task of copying full bibliographical information on every note card. You will have two sets of cards. One set will be your working bibliography, a list of sources; the other set will be notes on your reading, containing the information which will eventually be incorporated in your research paper.

The art of taking useful and accurate notes can be acquired only through practice. The following bits of advice, however, will help you avoid some common mistakes.

1. Use a separate card for each source.
2. Do not write on the back of cards.
3. Write facts and statistics in your own words.

4. If you copy the exact wording of the source, enclose in quotation marks everything copied. This is important. The use without quotation marks of the words of another writer is plagiarism and gives the impression that you are trying to pass the words off as your own. This is dishonest; in printed books it is a violation of the copyright law. Teachers know the style and vocabulary of which you are capable and are quick to note any signs of a mature writer or any rhetorical flights which are beyond the power of a high school student.

5. To speed the job of note-taking, you may use abbreviations and shorthand methods of your own, but do not use them for quoted matter. A quotation must be accurate to the last detail.

6. Be sure to write the page number of the source for every note you take.

Step 5. Organize notes and write the final outline.

The most time-consuming part of the preparation of a research paper is, of course, the reading and the taking of notes. Usually you should allot two or three weeks to this preparatory work. When you think you have gathered enough material to develop your subject adequately, you are ready to organize this material. Your preliminary outline may have undergone changes during your reading. When you found useful material which was not included in the outline, you changed the outline so as to include this material. If you did not find any material on a topic in your outline, you removed this topic. When all the slugs on your note cards are represented in your outline, arrange the cards in piles according to topics or slugs. Arranging the cards in this way assures that all cards containing information on the same outline topic will be together. Your research paper now begins to take shape.

The revised or final outline is to be handed in as part of your paper.

The Research Paper: The First Draft and Footnotes

Step 6. Write the first draft, including footnotes.

Having arranged your piles of cards in order, write the first draft of your paper. Remember to start with an introductory paragraph, stating the subject and explaining your selection of it. Bear in mind, as you write, what you have learned about paragraphing. Try to achieve smooth transitions both within paragraphs and between paragraphs. Your paper should also have at least one paragraph of conclusions, although the word "conclusion" does not appear as a topic in your outline.

Footnotes A research paper presents material which you have collected from many sources. You must give the sources of facts, statistics, and ideas. The accepted way to name your sources is to place them at the bottom of the pages in footnotes, where the reader may refer to them but where they will not disturb the continuity of the writing in the paper itself. Follow these procedures:

1. After a quotation, or another's idea, or facts from your sources, place slightly above the line a small numeral, beginning with 1 for each page of your paper, thus:[1].

2. At the bottom (foot) of the page and about a half-inch below the last line of text, place at the left margin the same number (in this instance, 1) and follow it with the source. A glance at the sample page from a high school research paper (p. 244) will make this clear.

Technicalities of footnoting must be strictly observed. While the information given in a footnote is much like that entered on a working bibliography card, there are certain differences in arrangement. The first footnote for any one source includes the following information, written with commas separating the items.

FOOTNOTE INFORMATION FOR A MAGAZINE OR NEWSPAPER ARTICLE

1. Author(s) (first name, or initials, *first*) unless article is unsigned
2. Title of article in quotes
3. Name of magazine or newspaper, underlined
4. Volume
5. Date
6. Page number from which the footnoted information was taken

   EXAMPLE 1. J. G. Meyer, "Those Airborne Chemicals," <u>Scientist and Citizen</u>, 10, August, 1968, p. 160.

FOOTNOTE INFORMATION FOR A BOOK

1. Author(s) (first name, or initials, *first*)
2. Title underlined
3. Page number

   EXAMPLE 2. Louis J. Battan, <u>The Unclean Sky; A Meteorologist Looks at Air Pollution</u>, p. 42.

240

Abbreviations in Footnotes When you refer more than once to the same source, do not repeat full information in footnotes after the first. To save time and space, use a short form to refer to the source and give the page number. For example, suppose that you have cited the following book in a footnote:

EXAMPLE 1. William Wise, Killer Smog: the World's Worst Air Pollution Disaster, p. 13.

Later you wish to cite the same book. All you need do is give the author's last name and the page number.

EXAMPLE 6. Wise, p. 60.

If you are using and footnoting more than one book by an author, you will have to give after the author's last name, the title of the book in short form. The footnote above, in such an instance, would read:

EXAMPLE 1. Wise, Killer Smog, p. 60.

If an article is unsigned, the footnote begins with the title:

EXAMPLE 2. "Why We'll All Breathe Easier," Nation's Business, 56, September, 1968, p. 66.

A subsequent reference to this article would read:

EXAMPLE 8. "Why We'll All Breathe Easier," p. 70.

Ibid. An easy way to refer to the same article that you have just referred to in a footnote is to use the Latin abbreviation *Ibid.,* which stands for *ibidem,* meaning "in the same (place)." Use *Ibid.* only when a reference to a source follows immediately after a reference to the same source.

EXAMPLE 1. William Wise, Killer Smog: the World's Worst Air Pollution Disaster, p. 35.
         2. Ibid., p. 36.

Note that *Ibid.* is underlined and, since it is an abbreviation, followed by a period.

If you wish to footnote an idea which the writer you were reading had, in turn, taken from another writer, use the following form:

EXAMPLE 7. Dr. Richard Prindle, quoted in "Menace in the Skies," Time, 89, January 27, 1967, p. 51.

---

1. William Wise, Killer Smog: the World's Worst Air Pollution Disaster, p. 13.
2. "Why We'll All Breathe Easier," Nation's Business, 56, September, 1968, p. 66.
3. Ibid., p. 67.
4. Wise, p. 26.

Footnotes at the foot of one page

EXERCISE The following five references appear in order as footnotes at the bottom of a single page of a research paper. The various items in each are deliberately written without regard for proper arrangement, quotes, underlining, or punctuation and capitals. On a separate sheet, write them as they should be written as footnotes, using *Ibid.* wherever appropriate.

1. A book by Perry, John, entitled Our Polluted World; Can Man Survive?, page 41.
2. An article entitled Breath of Death, written by F. Graham, Jr., which appeared in the July, 1968, issue of Audubon Magazine, volume 70. The reference is to page 51.
3. Same as 2, page 50.
4. Same as 1, page 65.
5. Same as 1, page 121.

The Research Paper: Final Draft and Bibliography

Step 7. Write the final draft and bibliography.

The final draft of your paper should represent your very best work. Try for clear organization, smooth transitions and good sentence structure, and absolute accuracy in the techniques of the research paper: outline, footnotes, and bibliography. Having already written a first draft, you should consider this final writing a kind of proof-reading, polishing exercise. Read your first draft carefully and preferably aloud so that unclear or clumsy sentences will be revealed. A sentence which you cannot read aloud easily and meaningfully obviously needs revision. Bring to bear on your first draft everything you know about punctuation and capitalization. A misspelled word is an inexcusable error in a research paper. Typewrite the paper if possible, double spacing the body of the paper, and single spacing the footnotes.

The Final Bibliography The bibliography which comes at the end of a research paper is a list of all the sources in your paper. It must be complete and accurate in details. It provides full information concerning your sources.

If you made your working bibliography carefully, you can follow the working bibliography cards in preparing the final bibliography. In the final bibliography the various sources are listed in alphabetical order by authors, and the information given for each is given in the same order as on your working bibliography cards. In effect, your bibliography has already been prepared. All you need do is arrange the cards in alphabetical order by authors' last names. Copy the information from the cards. Articles without authors are listed in alphabetical order with the first word of the title (except the words *a, an, the*) determining the alphabetical position. It is not necessary to number the items. Unless your teacher directs you to give the page number for books, you need not do so. The sample bibliography on the facing page will show you how yours should look. For a 2,000-word paper you should have at least six sources.

Bibliography

Battan, Louis J., <u>The Unclean Sky; a Meteorologist Looks at Air</u>
<u>Pollution</u>, Garden City, New York, Anchor Books, 1966.

<u>Effects of Air Pollution</u>, Washington, D.C., Department of Health,
Education, and Welfare, Public Health Service, 1967, ("Public
Health Service Bulletin" No. 1556).

Herber, Lewis, <u>Crisis in Our Cities</u>, Englewood Cliffs, New Jersey,
Prentice-Hall, 1965.

"Menace in the Skies," <u>Time</u>, 89:48-52, January 27, 1967.

Merson, B., "The Town That Refused to Die: Garrison, Mont., Faced
with Destruction by Smog and Air Pollution," <u>Good Housekeeping</u>,
168:80-1+, January, 1969.

Meyer, J. G., "Those Airborne Chemicals," <u>Scientist and Citizen</u>,
10:160-2, August, 1968.

Wise, William, <u>Killer Smog: the World's Worst Air Pollution Disaster</u>,
Chicago, Rand McNally, 1968.

Sample bibliography for a research paper

EXERCISE Each item in this exercise gives complete bibliographical information about a book or an article. On a separate sheet, revise the items so that they are correct in form and write them in the proper order and arrangement, as in a final bibliography.

1. A book by Donald Eaton Carr published by W. W. Norton and Company in New York in 1965, entitled Breath of Life.
2. An anonymous magazine article entitled Atmospheric Lead, which appeared in Scientist and Citizen for October 1968, volume 10, pages 199–205.
3. A pamphlet published by Humble Oil and Refining Company, Houston, Texas, in 1968, entitled You Can Help Keep Air and Water Clean.
4. A book entitled With Every Breath You Take by Howard R. Lewis, published in 1965 by Crown Publishers, New York.
5. A magazine article by C. H. Callison, which appeared in Audubon Magazine for January, 1968, entitled Congress and Conservation: Air Quality Act is Top 1967 Achievement, volume 70, page 56.

The first Federal action was the Air Pollution Act of 1955, in which Congress authorized research into the causes and cure of air pollution and offered to aid state and local governments in solving their air pollution problems. When it became clear that a major cause was motor vehicle exhaust, Congress passed in 1960 an amendment to the 1955 act, calling for the study of motor vehicle pollution. These legislative actions were further amended by the Clean Air Act of 1963 and the Air Quality Act of 1967.[1]

California had led the way in requiring installation of antipollution devices on automobiles. Since 1964 California law has required all cars to be equipped with a "blow-by", a device that "returns unburned gasoline in the crankcase back into the manifold." Since 1966 all cars sold in California have been equipped with devices to reduce 50% of the carbon monoxide emission from tailpipes.[2]

Federal legislation enacted in 1967 made these requirements nationwide.[3] The control of motor vehicle pollution is considered a federal rather than a local problem because motor vehicles travel interstate and pose the same problem everywhere. "Air pollution from stationary sources, such as factories, homes, and dumps, is considered primarily the responsibility of states and localities, because each place's problem is different."[4]

---

1. The Federal Air Pollution Program, p. 9.
2. "Menace in the Skies," Time, 89, January 27, 1967, p. 51.
3. The Federal Air Pollution Program, p. 12.
4. Gladwin Hill, "Government Plans National Parley as Part of Stepped-up Campaign Against Air Pollution," New York Times, September 28, 1966, p. 16.

Sample page from a research paper

INDEX

Abbreviations, in footnotes, 241
Address, inside, 226
Addresses, commas for, 47, 226
Adjective clauses, 20, 93
Adjective phrases, 13–14
Adjectives, 4, 12, 29
Adverb clauses, 20, 54, 90–91
Adverb phrases, 14, 54
Adverbs, 7
Agreement, of pronouns with antecedents, 141–42
of verbs with antecedents of relative pronouns, 140
of verbs with subjects, 134–35, 136, 139–40
Analogy, reasoning by, 222–23
And, faulty use of, 94–95
Antecedents of pronouns, 117–18, 141–42
Apostrophes, for contractions, 70
for possession, 67–69
Application, letter of, 228, 229
Appositive fragment, 79
Appositives, commas for, 46
subordination through, 96, 98
Argument, logical, 221–23

Be, forms of, 12, 153, 174 *ftn.*
Bibliography, for research paper, 242–43
Body of letter, 226, 227
Business letters, 226–30

Capitals, general uses of, 29–30, 32–33, 35–36, 65, 66
Card catalogue, 234
Case, nominative, 152–53, 159–60, 161–62
objective, 154–55, 159–60, 161–62
possessive, 67–68
Clauses, adjective, 20, 93
adverb, 20, 54, 90–91
defined, 16
essential, 51
independent, 16, 18–19, 54, 63
nonessential, 51
noun, 20
subordinate, *see* Subordinate clauses
Close of business letter, 226, 227
Collective nouns, number of, 139–40
Commas, general uses of, 44–45, 46–47, 51, 54, 64, 65
Common nouns, 3, 29
Comparison, paragraph developed by, 210
Complements, 11–12
Complex sentences, 19
Composition, description in, 199, 201, 202–03
figurative language in, 202–03
narration in, 199
outlining, 215–16
paragraphing, 215, 219, 220
planning, 198
proofreading, 198
revising, 198

sense words in, 201
See also Paragraphs
Complete predicate, 10
Complete subject, 10
Compound predicates, 10
Compound sentences, 18, 54
Compound subjects, 10, 136
Compound-complex sentences, 19
Conjunctions, compound sentences with, 54
coordinating, 8, 94–95
correlative, 8, 121–22
defined, 8
subordinating, 8, 16, 17, 90–91
Contractions, 70
Coordinating conjunctions, 8, 94–95
Correlative conjunctions, 8, 121–22

Dangling modifiers, 113
Dates, commas for, 47
Deductive reasoning, 221–22
Demonstrative pronouns, 4
Description, 199, 201, 202–03
Diagnostic test, 1–3
Dictionary of Contemporary American Usage, A, 132
Direct address, commas for, 46
Direct objects, 11
Direct quotations, 65

End marks, 44
Envelope, for business letter, 230
Essential clauses, 51
Essential phrases, 51
Events, capitals for, 32
Examples, paragraph developed by, 209–10
Exclamation points, 44, 65–66

Figurative language, 202–03
File, vertical, 235
Footnotes, for research paper, 240–41
Formal English, 131, 132, 133, 141, 153, 159
Fragments, sentence, 78–79
Future perfect tense, 174
Future tense, 174

Generalization, 222
Geographical names, capitals for, 30
Gerund phrase, 15
fragment, 79
Gerunds, 15

Heading of letter, 226, 227

Ibid., meaning of, 241
Incomplete constructions, pronoun use in, 164
Indefinite pronouns, 4
Independent clauses, 16, 18–19, 54, 63
Indirect objects, 11
Indirect quotations, 65
Inductive reasoning, 222
Infinitive phrase, 15
fragment, 79
Infinitives, 15

Informal English, 131, 132, 133, 141, 153, 159
Inquiry, letter of, 227, 228
Inside address of letter, 226, 227
Interrogative pronouns, 4
Interrupters, commas for, 46–47
Introductory expressions, 54
Irregular verbs, 174–75

Letters, application, 228, 229
business, 226–27, 228, 229, 230
inquiry, 227, 228
parts of, 226–27
Library research, 234–36
Lie, lay, use of, 179–80
Line of reasoning, 221–23
Linking verbs, 6
Logical argument, 221–23

Margins in letter, 227
Metaphor, defined, 203
Modifiers, dangling, 113
misplaced, 111–12
See also Adjectives; Adverbs

Narrative, personal, 199
Nationalities, capitals for, 35
Nominative case, 152–53, 159–60, 161–62
Nonessential clauses, 51
Nonessential phrases, 51
Nonstandard English, 131, 132, 133
Note-taking for research paper, 237–39
Noun clauses, 20
Nouns, collective, 139–40
common, 3, 29
defined, 3
plural, *see* Plural nouns
possessive, 67–68, 69
proper, 3, 29

Objective case, 154–55, 159–60, 161–62
Objects, direct, 11
indirect, 11
of prepositions, 155, 160
Organizations, capitals for, 32
Outline, for longer composition, 215–16
for research paper, 237, 239

Paragraphing, 215, 219, 220
Paragraphs, development of, 208–10
order of ideas in, 207
structure of, 204–05, 207
topic, 215, 219
topic sentences in, 205–06
transitional expressions in, 212–13
transitions between, 220
Parallel construction, 119–20, 121–22, 216
Parenthetical expressions, 47
Participial phrase, 15, 54
fragment, 79
Participles, 14–15, 174, 175
Past participles, 15, 174, 175

245

INDEX OF VOCABULARY WORDS

(Page numbers refer to definitions in text)

CONSONANT SOUNDS AND THEIR COMMON SPELLINGS

Sound	At the Beginning	At the End
/p/	**p:** pie	**p:** rip; **pe:** ripe
/t/	**t:** ten	**t:** pet; **te:** date
/k/	**k:** kit; **c:** cold	**ck:** lick; **ke:** like
/ch/	**ch:** chin	**tch:** witch; **ch:** reach
/b/	**b:** bed	**b:** tub; **be:** tube
/d/	**d:** do	**d:** rid; **de:** ride
/g/	**g:** get	**g:** beg; **gue:** league
/j/	**j:** jet; **g:** gentle	**dge:** budge; **ge:** cage
/f/	**f:** fun; **ph:** phrase	**ff:** stuff; **fe:** life; **f:** beef; **ph:** paragraph
/v/	**v:** very	**ve:** save
/s/	**s:** see; **c:** center	**ss:** glass; **s:** bus; **se:** case; **ce:** rice
/z/	**z:** zoo	**z:** quiz; **zz:** buzz; **se:** rose; **ze:** sneeze
/sh/	**sh:** ship	**sh:** push
/zh/	**j:** Jacques	**ge:** rouge; (in the middle) **s:** treasure
/r/	**r:** run; **wr:** wrist; **rh:** rhyme	**r:** car; **re:** care
/l/	**l:** lose	**ll:** pill; **le:** smile; **l:** fail
/m/	**m:** move	**m:** Sam; **me:** same; **mb:** tomb
/n/	**n:** nose; **gn:** gnaw; **kn:** know	**n:** pin; **ne:** pine
/ng/		**ng:** strong; **n:** trunk
/th/	**th:** thick	**th:** path
/th̶/	**th:** then	**th:** smooth; **the:** bathe
/y/	**y:** you; **u** /y-ū /: use	
/w/	**w:** will; **o** /w-u/: one; **qu** /k-w/: quick	
/h/	**h:** hat; **wh:** who	

VOWEL SOUNDS AND THEIR COMMON SPELLINGS

Fourteen Vowel Sounds

Sounds	/i/	/e/	/a/	/u/	/o/
Spellings and Examples	**i:** hit	**e:** red **ea:** dead	**a:** cat	**u:** but **o:** son	**o:** top **a:** far

Sounds	/ī/	/ē/	/ā/	/ū/	/ō/
Spellings and Examples	**VCe:** line **igh:** high **y:** try **ie:** die	**VCe:** Pete **ee:** deed **ea:** heat **e:** he **ie:** chief **ei:** deceive	**VCe:** lame **ai:** wait **ay:** pay **ei:** weigh	**VCe:** June **oo:** root **ew:** few **ue:** Sue **o:** to	**VCe:** lone **oa:** goat **ow:** slow **oe:** hoe **o:** no

Sounds	/o͞o/	/ou/	/oi/	/au/
Spellings and Examples	**oo:** look **u:** push	**ou:** out **ow:** cow	**oi:** oil **oy:** toy	**au:** haul **aw:** flaw **a:** ball **o:** long **ough:** fought **augh:** caught

The Vowel Sound Schwa /ə/

	i	e	ea	u	o
In Words of One Syllable	stir girl	were her	learn earth	burn spur	world worse

	-er	-or	-ar
The Sounds /ə-r/	runner maker father	actor orator navigator	beggar liar sugar

	-al	-le	-el	-ul	-ile	-il
The Sounds /ə-l/	legal moral rural	steeple battle circle	camel satchel travel	beautiful useful helpful	fertile juvenile hostile	April evil council

	-en	-an	-ain	-in
The Sounds /ə-n/	frozen deepen oaken garden	American orphan woman organ	captain curtain mountain certain	robin cabin basin cousin